Dandy Booksellers has listed RAF personnel details of senior officers (1-star rank
and above) serving in the RAF as of the 4th January 2018. Every precaution has been
taken to make sure that the information contained in the RAF list is correct at the time
of publication. We cannot accept any liability for errors or omissions. Please note that
data relating to major Defence and Air Force appointments, detailed in the pages prior
to the air rank listing, was correct as of the 31st March 2018 unless otherwise stated.
Applications for reproduction should be made in writing to Dandy Booksellers Ltd,
Units 3 & 4, 31-33 Priory Park Road, London NW6 7UP.

ISBN-13 978-1-78776-006-6

Published by Dandybooksellers Ltd and available from:

Online

www.dandybooksellers.com

Mail, Telephone, Fax & Email

Dandy Booksellers Ltd

Units 3 & 4, 31-33 Priory Park Road, London NW6 7UP

Telephone orders / General enquiries: +44 (0)20 7624 2993

Fax orders: +44 (0)20 7624 5049

Email: enquiries@dandybooksellers.com

Published by Dandy Booksellers Limited

Typesetting by Dandy Booksellers Limited

Printed in the UK by Dandy Booksellers Limited

CONTENTS

iv

NOTES

This is an abridged edition of the Air Force List produced under the Open Government Licence V.3 using source information provided by the Ministry of Defence. Defence service appointments in the pages prior to the air rank list may be found to be incomplete due to limited availablility of data. Where known, appointments have been included (sourced from Ministry of Defence supplements of The London Gazette and other official websites including www.raf.mod.uk and www.gov.uk). Additionally, some information that was detailed in last official edition of the Air Force List has not been supplied, specifically:

RAF Centre of Aviation Medicine
AWC/DEWC
RAF Elements Abroad
RAF Personnel in NATO Headquarters
Committees
Civil Consultants
Honorary Civil Consultants
Warrant Officers
Non-Commissioned Aircrew
Royal Air Force Reserve
Royal Auxiliary Air Force
List of Prizewinners
Retired List-Royal Air Force
Retired List Obituary

Notice of Change
- Graduation List

In November 2015, the disclosure policy of the Ministry of Defence was amended under the First Data Protection Principle in the Data Protection Act 1998 whereby RAF officers below 1 star rank will no longer be made available. The graduation list in this edition therefore details RAF senior officers (1-star rank and above) serving in the RAF as of the 4th January 2018.

The Gradation List show seniority in existing substantive ranks. All officers with a common seniority date are shown in alphabetical order. Acting rank is shown only for Air Officers. Entries include honours and awards (as shown on Pages vi-vii) and symbols relating to certain courses (as shown on Pages viii-ix). In addition, certain academic and professional qualifications are shown, although not necessarily a complete list of those held on official records.

Correspondence to the Editor should be addressed to:

Miss C R Hooper

Editor of the RAF List

Dandy Booksellers Ltd

Units 3 & 4, 31-33 Priory Park Road

London NW6 7UP

Telephone: +44 (0)20 7624 2993

Fax: +44 (0)20 7624 5049

Email: enquiries@dandybooksellers.com

Web: www.dandybooksellers.com

LETTERS DENOTING HONOURS AND AWARDS IN ORDER OF PRECEDENCE

VC	Victoria Cross
GC	George Cross
KG	Knight of the Order of the Garter
KT	Knight of the Order of the Thistle
KP	Knight of the St Patrick
GCB	Knight Grand Cross or Dame Grand Cross of the Order of the Bath
OM	Member of the Order of Merit
GCSI	Knight Grand Commander of the Star of India
CI	Order of the Crown of India
GCMG	Knight Grand Cross of the Order of St Michael and St George
GCVO	Knight Grand Cross or Dame Grand Cross of the Royal Victorian Order
GBE	Knight Grand Cross or Dame Grand Cross of the Order of the British Empire
CH	Member of the Order of the Companion of Honour
KCB	Knight Commander of the Order of the Bath
DCB	Dame Commander of the Order of the Bath
KCSI	Kinght Commander of the Order of Star of India
KCMG	Knight Commander of the Order of St Michael and St George
DCMG	Dame Commander of the Order of St Michael and St George
KCIE	Knight Commander of the Order of the Indian Empire
KCVO	Knight Commander of the Royal Victorian Order
DCVO	Dame Commander of the Royal Victorian Order
KBE	Knight Commander of the Order of the British Empire
DBE	Dame Commander of the Order of the British Empire
CB	Companion of the Order of the Bath
CSI	Companion of the Order of the Star of India
CMG	Companion of the Order of St Michael and St George
CIE	Companion of the Order of the Indian Empire
CVO	Commander of the Royal Victorian Order
CBE	Commander of the Order of the British Empire
DSO	Companion of the Distinguished Service Order
LVO	Lieutenant of the Royal Victorian Order
OBE	Officer of the Order of the British Empire
ISO	Companion of the Imperial Service Order
MVO	Member of the Royal Victorian Order
MBE	Member of the Order of the British Empire
CGC	Conspicuous Gallantry Cross
RRC	Member of the Royal Red Cross
DSC	Distinguished Service Cross
MC	Military Cross
DFC	Distinguished Flying Cross
AFC	Air Force Cross
ARRC	Associate of the Royal Red Cross
DCM	Distinguished Conduct Medal
CGM	Conspicuous Gallantry Medal
GM	George Medal
DSM	Distinguished Service Medal
MM	Military Medal
DFM	Distinguished Flying Medal
QGM	The Queen's Gallantry Medal
BEM	British Empire Medal
RVM	Royal Victoria Medal
QVRM	Queen's Volunteer Reserves Medal
ERD	Army Emergency Reserve Decoration
TD	Territorial Decoration or Efficiency Decoration (Obsolescent)
RD	Royal Naval Reserve Officer's Decoration
AE	Air Efficiency Award
•	Denotes the award of a bar to a decoration or medal for gallantry. The award of an additional bar is indicated by the addition of a further star for each reward.

Note: When the recipient of an Order of Knighthood is promoted to a higher rank within the same Order, the lower rank is absorbed in the higher and therefore the designation of the lower rank is omitted after the name.

OTHER HONOURS AND AWARDS

AK   Knight of Australia
QSO Queen's Service Order (New Zealand)

LETTER DENOTING APPOINTMENTS TO THE QUEEN

ADC   .....Aide-de Camp
QHDS ....Honorary Dental Surgeon
QHS Honorary Surgeon

QHP Honorary Physician
QHC ......Honorary Chaplain
QHN ......Queen's Honorary Nurse

EXPLANATIONS OF ABBREVIATIONS AND SYMBOLS
SHOWN IN GRADATION LISTS

a   Qualified at Specialist Armament Course.

ac   Qualified in Aircraft Control.

adp   Qualified Advanced Automatic Data Processing Course.

ae   Qualified Aero-Systems Engineering Course.

ais   Qualified at Advanced Information Systems.

amec ......Qualified Advanced Maintenance Engineering Course. (from Course 8).

asq   Qualified GD Aero-Systems Course.

awcc ......Graduates of the Air Warfare Commanders' Course, at the Department of Air Warfare. Royal Air Force College Cranwell (including graduates of the Royal Air Force College of Air Warfare Course at the Royal Air Force Flying College).

aws   Graduates of the Air Warfare Course, at the Department of Air Warfare. Royal Air Force College Cranwell (including graduates of the Royal Air Force College of Air Warfare and graduates of the Air Warfare Course at the Royal Air Force Flying College).

ax   Qualified at Advanced Armament Course.

cfs*   General Duties Officers and Master Pilots who have qualified as flying instructors and who hold a Central Flying School A1 instructor category.

cfs   General Duties Officers and Master Pilots who have qualified as flying instructors and who hold a Central Flying School A2 instructor category.

cfs(ae)* ..Qualified Air Electronic Operator Instructors of A1 instructor category.

cfs(ae) ....Qualified Air Electronic Operator Instructors of A2 instructor category.

cfs(c)* ...General Duties Officers and Master Aircrew who have qualified as crewman instructors and who hold a Central Flying School A 1 instructor category.

cfs{c} .....General Duties Officers and Master Aircrew who have qualified as crewman instructors and who hold a Central Flying School A2 instructor category.

cfs(e)* ...Qualified Air Engineer Instructors of A1 instructor category.

cfs(e) .....Qualified Air Engineer Instructors of A2 instructor category.

cfs(g)* ...Qualified Gliding Instructors of A1 instructor category.

cfg(g) .....Qualified Gliding Instructors of A2 instructor category.

cfs(n)* ...General Duties Officers who have qualified as navigation instructors and who hold a Central Flying School A 1 instructor category.

cfs(n) .....General Duties Officers who have qualified as navigation instructors and who hold a Central Flying School A2 instructor category.

cfs(pn)* ..Qualified Pilot Navigator Instructors of A1 instructor category.

cfs(pn) ...Qualified Pilot Navigator Instructors of A2 instructor category.

cfs(r)* ....Qualified Rearcrew Instructors of A 1 instructor category.

cfs(r) ......Qualified Rearcrew Instructors of A2 instructor category.

cfs(t)* ....Qualified Tactics Instructors of A1 instructor category.

cfs(t) ......Qualified Tactics Instructors of A2 instructor category.

df*   Officers who have completed a Royal Air Force Diamond Jubilee Fellowship.

df   Officers who have completed Defence Fellowships.

e   Qualified at Specialist Engineering Course.

e(t)   Qualified at Specialist Engineering followed by Torpedo Course.

etps   Graduate of the Empire Test Pilot's School.

ex   Qualified at University Course in Engineering in addition to qualifying e.

fc .... Qualified in Fighter Control.

G† .... Qualified at Army Long Gunnery Staff Course (AA).

Glal   Qualified at the Army Gunnery Staff Course, Air Defence.

gw   Qualified at Advanced Guided Weapons Course or Advanced Weapons Course at the Royal Air Force Technical College or the Guided Weapons Course at the Royal Military College of Science or the Graduate Astronautics Course at the United States Air Force Institute of Technology, Dayton, Ohio.

hcsc   Qualified at Higher Command & Staff course.

hlaq   Higher Level Academic Qualification.

i*   Qualified as 1st class interpreter/ Diploma 1st class pass.

i   Qualified as 2nd class interpreter/ Diploma 2nd class pass.

icc   Graduate of the Police Staff College (Bramshilll Intermediate Command Course.

idc   Graduate of the Imperial Defence College, prior to 17 January 1971; or has held an appointment as Commandant or Instructor at the college for a period of one year.

ifp   International Fellows Programme at the National Defence University in Washington DC.

im   Supply Officers qualified at an Industrial Management/Management Science Course at Manchester University.

jsdc Graduate of the Joint Service Defence College.

jssc Graduate of the Joint Services Staff College, prior to 6 August 1971.

met Qualified at University Course in Meteorology.

n Qualified at Specialists Navigation Course.

nadc Graduate of the NATO Defence College.

ndc Graduate of the National Defence College.

nx Qualified at Advanced Specialists Navigation Course.

Graduate of the:

oaws(US)................United States Air War College.

ocds(Can) ....Canadian National Defence College.

ocds(Ind) ....Indian National Defence College.

odc(Aus) ....Australian Joint Service Staff College.

odc (US) ....United States Armed Forces Staff College
United States Navy War College.

odc(Fr) / osc(Fr) ....Cours Superieure Interarmes.
(to include French Ecole Superieure de Geurre).

ode(Ge) / osc(Ge) ..Command and General Staff College of the Federal German Armed Forces.

osc(Ku)...Graduate of the Kuwaiti Staff Course.

osc(US) ..United States Air Command and Staff College.

pfc Graduate of the RAPC Long Finance and Accountancy Course.

ph Qualified at Specialist Photographic Course.

pi Qualified in Photographic Interpretation duties.

pji Qualified as a parachutist Instructor.

ppetc ......Long Petroleum Course.

psc Royal Air Force Graduates of the Royal Air Force Staff College and Foreign and Commonwealth Staff Colleges approved by the Director General of RAF Training.

psc(a) .....Royal Navy and Army graduates of Royal Air Force Staff College.

psc(Aus)..RAAF Staff College, Canberra.

psc(Aus)..Australian Joint Service Staff College, Canberra.

psc(Can)..Canadian Forces Command and Staff College, Toronto.

psc{Fr) ...College Interarmees de Defense, Paris.

psc(Ge)...Fuhrungsakademie der Bundeswehr, Hamburg.

psc(Ind) ..Indian Defence Services Staff College, Wellington.

psc(j) ......Graduate of Joint Services Command & Staff College.

psc(m} ....Royal Air Force graduates of the Army Staff College.

psc(n)......Royal Air Force graduates of the Royal Naval Staff College.

psc(Spa) ..Escuela Superior del Air, Madrid.

psc(US)...United States Command and Staff College, Maxwell AFB.

psm Advanced Certificates of the Royal Military School of Music.

ptsc Graduate of the Royal Military College of Science.

qab Qualified Air Battle.

qas Graduate of the full Aerosystems Course (Aerosystems qualified).

qcc Qualified at Officers Command Courses.

qhti Qualified Helicopter Tactics Instructor.

qsb Qualified Support Battlestaff Course.

qs Qualified Staff.

qss* Qualified Staff Studies. (2 year course).

qss Qualified Staff Studies. (118 months course).

qss2 Qualified Staff Studies Module 2.

qss1 Qualified Staff Studies Module 1.

qtm Qualified Targeting and Mission Support Course.

qwi Qualified Weapons Instructor.

qwi(AD).Qualified Weapons Instructor (Air Defence).

qwi(H) ...Qualified Weapons Instructor (Hawk).

qwi(SAW)Qualified Weapons Instructor (Surface-to-Air Weapons).

qwi(T) ...Qualified Weapons Instructor (Tornado).

reds Graduate of the Royal College of Defence Studies.

rcds(FM) .Royal College of Defence Studies Foundatio Medal.

s Qualified at Specialist Signals Course.

sec Graduate of the Police Staff College (Bramshilll Strategic Command Course.

semc ......Qualified Senior Engineering Management Course.

slmc Senior Logistics Management Course.

snc Qualified Staff Navigation Course. (Series beginning April, 1957).

sowc ......Qualified at Senior Officers War Course. Royal Naval War College.

ssc Senior Supply Course.

sx Qualified at University Course in Electrical Engineering and Wireless Telegraphy in addition to qualifying s.

TIG(a) ...Trained in Gunnery (Air Defence).

tp Pilot graduate of the Empire Test Pilots' School IETPS). United States Air Force Test Pilots' School (USAFtps), United States Navy Test Pilots' School (USNtps), or French Ecole du Personnel Navigant d'Essais et de Reception (EPNER).

ts Supply Officers who have completed the Cranfield Institute of Technology MSc course in Transport Studies.

w Qualified at the Senior Weapons Course.

RAF BRANCHES AND SYMBOLS DENOTING AIRCREW CATEGORY AND SPECIALIZATION WITHIN BRANCHES

FUNCTIONAL BRANCHES

Flying Branch (Fg):
(P) ......Pilot
(N) ......Navigator
(RPAS(P)) ....Remotely Piloted Air System (Pilot)
(AEO) ....Air Electronics Officer
(ENG) ....Engineer
(ALM) ....Air Load master
(WSO) ....Weapons Systems Officer
(WSOp) ....Weapons Systems Operator

Operations Support Branch:
(ATC) ....Air Traffic control
(ABM)....................Aerospace Battle Manager
(INT) ....Intelligence
(FLTOPS) ....Flight Operations
(REGT) ....Regiments
(PROVSY) .... Provost Security

Engineer Branch (Eng):
(AS) ......Aerosystems
(CE) ......Communications-Electronics

Logistics Branch (Logs)

Personnel Branch (Pers):
(SPT) ....Support
(TRG) ....Training
(PEd) ....Physical Education

SPECIALIST RAF BRANCHES

Medical Branch
Dental Branch
Medical Support Officer Branch (MSO)
Chaplains Branch
Legal Branch
Nursing Officer Branch
Directors of Music (DOM)

SYMOBLS DENOTING RAF TRADES AND TRADE TRAINING SCHOOLS

Aircraft Engineering

DCAE, RAF Cosford

Aircraft Engineering Technician .... A Eng Tech
Aircraft Technician (Avionics) .... A Tech(Av)
Aircraft Technician (Mechanical) .... A Tech(M)
Aircraft Maintenance Mechanic (Avionics) .... AMM(Av)
Aircraft Maintenance Mechanic (Mechanical) .... AMM(M)
Engineering Technician Weapon .... Eng Tech W
Weapon Technician .... W Tech

Information and Communications Technology

DSCIS, No 1 Radio School, RAF Cosford
DSCIS, No 1 Radio School, AES, RAF Digby

Information and Communications Technology
   Manager ....ICTM
Information and Communications Technology
   Technician ....ICT Tech
Information and Communications Technology
   Aerial Erector ....ICT Al Erect

General Engineering

DSEME, MOD Lyneham

General Engineering Technician .... Gen Eng Tech
General Technician Electrical .... Gen Tech E
General Technician (Mechanical) .... Gen Tech(M)
General Technician Workshops .... Gen Tech WS

Logistics

Defence School of Transport, Leconfield

Logistics (Driver) .... Logs (MTD)

Force Protection

RAF Police .... RAFP
   (Joint Police School, Southwick Park)
Gunner .... Gnr
   (RAF Regt Depot, RAF Honington)
Firefighter .... Fftr
   (DFTDC, RAF Manston)

Air Traffic Control

CATCS, RAF Shawbury

Air Traffic Controller .... ATC
Air Traffic Control Assistant .... ATCA
Flight Operations Manager .... FOM
Flight Operations Assistant .... FOA

Meteorological Observer .... Met Obsvr
   (RAF Reserve Mobile Met Unit)

General Service

Trainee .... Trn
   (Recruit Training Squadron, RAF Halton)
RAF Physical Training Instructor .... RAF PTI
   (RAF School of Physical Training, RAF Cosford)

Intelligence

JITG, HQ Chicksands

Intelligence Analyst .... Int An
Intelligence Analyst (Voice) (Includes Student (Sdt) trade)
   .... Int An(V)

Aerospace Systems Operating

SABM, RAF Boulmer

Aerospace Systems Manager .... AS Mngr
Aerospace Systems Operator .... AS Op
SNCO Weapons Control .... SNCO Wpns Ctl

Safety and Surface

Survival Equipment Fitter .... SE Fitt
   (DCAE, RAF Cosford)
Painter and Finisher .... Ptr & Fnr
   (No 4 SofTT, MOD St Athan)

Photography

JITG - DSOP, HQ Chicksands

Photographer .... Photo
   (DSOP, RAF Cosford)
Air Cartographer .... Air Cart
   (No 1 AIDU, RAF Northolt)

ROYAL AIR FORCE

"Per Ardua ad Astra"

THE QUEEN

Air Commodore-in-Chief..Royal Auxiliary Air Force (1.6.53)
Air Commodore-in-Chief..Royal Air Force Regiment (1.6.53)
Commandant-in-Chief..Royal Air Force College, Cranwell (27.5.60)
Royal Honorary Air Commodore...Royal Air Force Marham (11.6.77)
Royal Honorary Air Commodore.......................................No 603 (City of Edinburgh) Squadron RAuxAF (1.12.00)

Commonwealth Forces

Air Commodore-in-Chief..Air Reserve of Canada, Royal Australian Air Force Reserve,
Territorial Air Force (of New Zealand)

Private Secretary to HM The Queen
The Rt Hon Edward Young *CVO*
Office: Buckingham Palace, London SW1A 1AA Tel: 020 7930 4832

MEMBERS OF THE ROYAL FAMILY

His Royal Highness The Prince Philip, Duke of Edinburgh,
KG KT OM GCVO GBE ONZ QSO AK GCL CC CMM

Marshal of the Royal Air Force ....(15.1.53)
Royal Honorary Air Commodore...Royal Air Force Northolt (1.8.12)

Commonwealth Forces

Marshal of the Royal Australian Air Force
Marshal of the Royal New Zealand Air Force
General, Royal Canadian Air Force
Air Commodore-in-Chief Royal Canadian Air Cadets

His Royal Highness The Prince of Wales, KG KT GCB OM AK QSO PC ADC(P)

Marshal of the Royal Air Force ....(16.06.12)
Royal Honorary Air Commodore...Royal Air Force Valley (1.4.93)

Commonwealth Forces

Air Commodore-in-Chief Royal New Zealand Air Force
Colonel-in-Chief Air Reserve (of Canada)

Her Royal Highness The Duchess of Cornwall GCVO

Royal Honorary Air Commodore..Royal Air Force Halton (10.9.08)
Royal Honorary Air Commodore...Royal Air Force Leeming (10.9.08)

His Royal Highness The Duke of Cambridge, KG KT ADC

Squadron Leader ....(1.1.16)
Royal Honorary Air Commandant ....Royal Air Force Coningsby (10.9.08)

Her Royal Highness The Duchess of Cambridge

Honorary Air Commandant...Air Cadets Organisation (17.12.15)

His Royal Highness Prince Henry of Wales, KCVO

Royal Honorary Air Commandant .... Royal Air Force Honington (10.9.08)

His Royal Highness The Duke of York, KG GCVO ADC(P)

Royal Honorary Air Commodore .... Royal Air Force Lossiemouth (15.9.96)

His Royal Highness The Earl of Wessex, KG GCVO ADC(P)

Royal Honorary Air Commodore .... Royal Air Force Waddington (10.9.08)

Her Royal Highness The Countess of Wessex GCVO

Royal Honorary Air Commodore .... Royal Air Force Wittering (10.9.08)

Her Royal Highness The Princess Royal, KG KT GCVO QSO

Royal Honorary Air Commodore .... Royal Air Force Brize Norton (1.10.11)
Royal Honorary Air Commodore .... University of London Air Squadron (2.9.93)

His Royal Highness The Duke of Gloucester, KG GCVO

Honorary Air Marshal .... (1.9.96)
Royal Honorary Air Commodore .... Royal Air Force Odiham (1.4.93)
Royal Honorary Air Commodore .... No 501 (County of Gloucester) Squadron Royal Auxiliary Air Force (5.6.01)

His Royal Highness The Duke of Kent, KG GCMG GCVO ADC(P)

Honorary Air Chief Marshal .... (1.7.96)

His Royal Highness Prince Michael of Kent, GCVO

Honorary Air Marshal .... Royal Air Force Benson (1.3.12)

Her Royal Highness Princess Alexandra, The Hon. Lady Ogilvy, KG GCVO

Patron and Air Chief Commandant .... Princess Mary's Royal Air Force Nursing Service (1.11.66)

APPOINTMENTS TO THE QUEEN
(as of 31st Mar 18)

Air Aide-de-Camp to The Queen
Air Chief Marshal Sir Stephen Hillier KCB CBE DFC .... 11 Jul 16

Aides-de-Camp to The Queen
Air Commodore R. A. Williams OBE ADC MA BA FCILT ....01 Jan 07
Air Vice Marshal (Retd.) D. M. Niven CB CBE .... 01 Sep 11
Group Captain R. D. Pratley .... 25 Jul 15
Group Captain R. A. Davies .... 31 Jul 15
Group Captain I. Laing .... 23 Oct 15
Group Captain A. P. Marshall OBE .... 04 Mar 16
Air Vice Marshal R. Paterson CB OBE .... 01 Jun 16
Group Captain D. C. Tait MBE ....01 Jan 17
Group Captain K. D. Taylor ....01 Feb 17
Air Vice-Marshal Lord Beaverbrook .... 13 Mar 17
Group Captain M. H. G. Carver .... 29 Jul 17

Equerry
Wing Commander Samuel Fletcher, RAF *(until Jul 17)*

Extra Equerries to The Queen
Air Commodore the Hon. Sir Timothy Elworthy, KCVO CBE
Group Captain Tim Hewlett, LVO OBE
Air Marshal Sir David Walker, KCVO OBE

Honorary Chaplains to The Queen
The Reverend (Group Captain) Jonathan P. M. Chaffey, QHC MA BA RAF .... 01 Jun 12
The Reverend (Wing Commander) D. T. Osborn, QHC .... 28 Jun 14
The Reverend (Group Captain) J. R. Ellis ....06 May 17
The Reverend (Wing Commander) P. Mellor ....01 Feb 18

Honorary Physicans to The Queen
Air Commodore S. C. Kilbey, MA MB ChB MRCGP DOccMed DAvMed DRCOG DFFP CMgr FCMI ....01 Feb 15
Air Commodore A. N. C. Reid, MB ChB MSC DRCOG DAvMed FFOM ....06 Apr 15
Group Captain A. D. Green, MB BS MRCP .... 15 Feb 16
Group Captain C. S. Walton .... 31 Mar 16

Honorary Surgeons to The Queen
Group Captain D. Gradwell .... 05 Mar 12
Group Captain N. McGuire .... 01 Apr 12
Group Captain I. D. Sargeant OBE RAF ....31 Dec 16
Air Commodore R. D. J. Withnall MA MBBS MSc (Primary Care) FRCGP DRCOG DFFP MRAeS FCMI RAF ....06 Nov 17
Air Commodore D. C. McLoughlin OBE MB MCh BAO MSc MRCGP FFOM DRCOG DAvMed RAF .... 06 Nov 17

Honorary Dental Surgeons to The Queen
Group Captain T. W. Jones, MSc BDS MFGDP (UK) RAF .... 01 Feb 15
Air Commodore M. Byford BDS MFGDP (UK) MA RAF ....02 Dec 16

Honorary Nurse to The Queen
Group Captain M. J. Priestley *(until Aug 18)* .... 10 Aug 15

FOREIGN SOVEREIGNS
AND
MEMBERS OF FOREIGN ROYAL FAMILIES
who hold Honorary Commissions in the Royal Air Force

Air Chief Marshal HM The Sultan of Brunei Darussalam, GCB GCMG ....5 Nov 92

DEFENCE COUNCIL

Secretary of State for Defence (Chairman of the Defence Council)
The Right Honourable Gavin Williamson *CBE MP* ....02 Nov 17

Minister of State for Defence and Deputy Leader of the House of Lords (Unpaid)
The Right Honourable EARL HOWE *MP* ....May 15

Minister of State for the Armed Forces
The Right Honourable MARK LANCASTER *TD MP* ....13 Jun 17

Parliamentary Under Secretary of State and Minister for Defence People and Veterans
The Right Honourable Mr TOBAIS ELLWOOD *MP* ....14 Jun 17

Permanent Secretary of State
Mr STEPHEN LOVEGROVE *CB*

Chief of the Defence Staff
Air Chief Marshal Sir STUART PEACH *GBE KCB ADC DL BA MPhil DTech DLitt FRAeS RAF*

First Sea Lord and Chief of Naval Staff
Admiral Sir PHILIP JONES *KCB ADC*

Chief of the General Staff
General Sir NICHOLAS PATRICK CARTER *KCB CBE DSO ADC Gen*

Chief of the Air Staff
Air Chief Marshal Sir STEPHEN HILLIER *KCB CBE DFC ADC MA RAF*

Vice Chief of the Defence Staff
General Sir GORDON MESSENGER *KCB DSO* OBE ADC*

Commander of Joint Forces Command
General Sir CHRIS DEVERELL *KCB MBE ADC Gen*

Director General Finance
Ms Cat Little

AIR FORCE BOARD OF THE DEFENCE COUNCIL

Civilian

The Right Honourable *Sir* GAVIN WILLIAMSON *CBE MP*
Secretary of State for Defence
(Chairman of the Defence Council and Chairman of the Army Board of the Defence Council)

The Right Honourable Colonel MARK LANCASTER *TD MP*
Minister of State for the Armed Forces

Mr Guto Bebb *MP*
Minister of State for Defence Procurement

The Right Honourable Mr TOBAIS ELLWOOD *MP*
Parliamentary Under Secretary of State and Minister for Defence People and Veterans

Air Force Board Standing Committee

CHIEF OF THE AIR STAFF
Air Chf Mshl *Sir* STEPHEN HILLIER *KCB CBE DFC ADC MA RAF*

CHIEF OF THE AIR STAFF'S WARRANT OFFICER
WO JON CROSSLEY

ASSISTANT CHIEF OF THE AIR STAFF
AVM MIKE WIGSTON *CBE RAF*

DEPUTY COMMANDER OPERATIONS
AM STUART D ATHA *CB DSO*

DEPUTY COMMANDER CAPABILITY AND AIR MEMBER FOR PERSONNEL AND CAPABILITY
AM SEAN K P REYNOLDS *CBE DFC*

AIR MEMBER FOR MATERIEL AND CHIEF OF MATERIEL (AIR)
AM JULIAN A YOUNG *CB OBE RAF*

COMMANDANT GENERAL ROYAL AUXILIARY AIR FORCE
THE RT HON AVM LORD BEAVERBROOK

CHIEF OF STAFF PERSONNEL AND AIR SECRETARY
AVM CHRISTINA R ELLIOT *CBE RAF*

DIRECTOR OF RESCOURCES (AIR)
Mr CHARLIE PATE

(Specialist officers as required - data unavailable)

HEAD OFFICE AND CORPOATE SERVICES
(as of 31st March 2018)

CHIEF OF DEFENCE STAFF

Chief of the Defence Staff	ACM *Sir* Stuart Peach *GBE KCB ADC DL*	140716
Chief of the Defence Staff Principal Staff Officer	Brig Ian S Mortimer	Sep 16
Secretary Chiefs of Staff Committee	Col Timothy F Law	Dec 15
Vice Chief of the Defence Staff	Gen Sir Gordon Messenger *KCB DSO** *OBE CB ADC*	May 16
Defence Senior Adviser Middle East	Lt Gen Tom Beckett *CBE (until Jan 18)* Lt Gen *Sir* John Lorimer *KCB DSO MBE (from Jan 18)*	060115
Service Complaints Ombudsman	Nicola Williams	010116
Head of Defence Operational Capability	Brig James Woodham	Aug 17

MILITARY STRATEGY AND OPERATIONS

Deputy Chief of Defence Staff (Military Strategic Operations)	Lt Gen Mark A P Carleton-Smith *CBE*	Apr 16
Assistant Chief of Defence Staff (Defence Engagement)	Maj Gen Giles Patrick Hill *CBE*	Apr 17
Head Defence Engagement Strategy	Air Cdre James Linter *OBE (until Sep 17)*	
Head of International Policy & Planning (Military)	Brig Stephen C McMahon *CBE*	Apr 16
Head of International Policy & Planning (Civilian)	N/D	
Head International Policy & Planning Sub-Saharan Africa	Brig David J Eastman	May 17
Assistant Chief of Defence Staff (Operations)	AVM Andrew M Turner *CBE*	Oct 17
Head Military Strategic Effects	Air Cdre Jonathan Burr *CBE DFC (until Apr 18)* Air Cdre Nigel J Colman *OBE (from Apr 18)*	Jul 15
Head Operations Policy	Lisa Wain	
Head Afghanistan, Pakistan, Iraq and Syria Policy	N/D	
Head Afghanistan, Pakistan, Iraq and Syria Military	N/D	
Head Special Forces & Intelligence Strategy & Operations	N/D	
Head Operations Military	Brig G Stickland *DSO MBE (until Dec 18)*	
Head Defence Intelligence Regional & Thematics	Air Cdre Steven R Thornber *CBE*	290118
Director of Operational Policy	Dominic Wilson	
Director of Special Forces	Maj Gen James Chiswell *CBE MC*	

BRITISH DEFENCE STAFF - UNITED STATES (BDS-US)
British Embassy Washington, 3100 Massachusetts Avenue NW, Washington DC 20008, USA
(Tel: +1 202 588 6500   Email: BDSUS-COMMUNICATIONS@mod.uk)

Head of BDS-US/Defence Attaché	AVM Gavin D A Parker *OBE MA BSc RAF*	Jun 17
Minister (Defence Materiel, USA)	Steve McCarthy	Sep 14
Deputy Director Commonwealth Integration, Washington	AVM Sean Corbett *MBE (until Jan 18)*	Oct 15
Senior British Military Advisor to		
United States Central Command, Tampa	R Adm William N Entwisle *OBE MVO*	Jan 17
Naval Attaché	Cdre Martin J Connell *RN*	Sep 14
Military Attaché	Brig James Carr-Smith	Sep 16
Air Attaché	Air Cdre James Linter *OBE*	Sep 17
Councellor Defence Acquistion and Technology	Simon Gadd	Aug 15
Counsellor Defence Policy and Nuclear	Iain King *CBE*	Jan 16

Chief of the Defence Staff's Liaison Officer to the Chairman of the US Joint Chiefs of Staff	Air Cdre Michael J Smeath *MBE*	Jul 17
Royal Marine Attaché	Col Neil Sutherland *MBE RM*	Jul 16
Assistant Military Attaché	Lt Col Paul Bates	Aug 17
Assistant Air Attaché	Gp Capt Stephen Richards RAF	May 16

MILITARY CAPABILITY

Deputy Chief of Defence Staff (Military Capability)	Lt Gen Mark W Poffley *OBE*	Jan 16
Assistant Chief of Defence Staff (Capability & Force Design)	AVM Richard J Knighton *CB*	Jan 17
Head of Finance Military Capability - Plans	Brig Jeremy M J Bennett	Apr 16
Head of Finance Military Capability - Joint Plans	Air Cdre Richard C Maddison *OBE*	Jul 16
Head of Finance Military Capability - Strategy	Cdre Hugh Beard	
Head of Finance Military Capability - Infrastructure	N/D	
Director Carrier Strike	R Adm Matthew P Briers	Jan 18
Head Carrier Enabled Power Projection	Air Cdre Paul A Godfrey *OBE*	Oct 17
Director of Strategic Programmes	Richard Berthon	Jul 16
Head of Weapons, Evaluation & Capability Assurance	Dr Dai Morris	
Head Air Manoeuvre Capability (HQ Army)	Air Cdre Alastair P T Smith	Apr 17
Director National Shipbuilding Strategy	Ian Gibson	

DEFENCE PERSONNEL

Chief of Defence People	Lt Gen Richard E Nugee *CVO CBE*	Apr 16
Assistant Chief of Defence Staff (Personnel Capability) / Defence Services Secretary	AVM Garry Tunnicliffe	27 Jun 16
Head Defence People Strategy	Air Cdre Paul E O'Neill	Jan 18
Head Training Education Skills, Recruitment and Resettlement	Capt Mark Cameron *OBE*	Feb 18
Head Service Personnel Support	Helen Helliwell	
Assistant Chief Defence Staff (Reserves & Cadets)	Maj Gen Ranald T I Munro *CBE TD VR*	Apr 16
Head Youth and Cadets	Cdre Jonathan M S Fry	Jan 14
Head of Reserves Policy	Brig Gerhard H Wheeler	Mar 17
Assistant Chief of Staff Personnel Delivery	Air Cdre Gerard A Opie	111016
Director Service Personnel Policy	Heather McNaughton / Caroline Pusey	
Medical Adviser	N/D	
Head Secretariat	N/D	
Head Accommodation Policy	N/D	
Head Armed Forces Remuneration	James MacLeod	Sep 16
Head New Joiner Offer	N/D	
Head Armed Forces People Programme	Richard Vincent	
Director Service Prosecutions	Andrew Cayley *CMG QC FRSA*	031213
Deputy Director Service Prosecutions	Darren Reed	
Director Civilian Human Resources	Siobhan Sheirdan	

DEFENCE INNOVATION

Director Defence Innovation	Kristina Murrin	
Head Defence Innovation	N/D	

PERMANENT UNDER SECRETARY OF STATE (PUS)

(as of 31st March 2018)

Permanent Under Secretary of State ....Stephen Lovegrove *CB*

Secretary of State Chief of Staff ....Damian Parmenter

Chief Executive of Defence Electronics and Components Agency ...Geraint Spearing

Chief Executive of Defence Science and Technology Laboratory ....Gary Aitkenhead ....Dec 17

Director General Nuclear ....Julian Kelly

DEFENCE SCIENCE AND TECHNOLOGY

Chief Scientific Adviser ....Prof Hugh Durrant-Whyte

Chief Scientific Adviser (Nuclear)..Prof Robin Grimes

Defence Science & Technology Strategy Director ....Dr Simon Cholerton

Head International & Strategic Research..................................Dr Bryan Wells

Head Science Strategy...Dr Rob Sullivan

Head Portfolio...Dr Nicholas Joad

Head Customer Engagement..Andrew Caldwell

SECURITY POLICY

Director General Security Policy ....Peter Watkins *CBE*..Apr 14

Director General MOD Saudi Armed Forces Projects, Riyadh ....AVM Ian C Morrison *CBE (until Jan 18)*

AVM Martin E Sampson *CBE DSO (from Jan 18)*

Head of Programmes ....Air Cdre Simon J Harris *(until 260418)* ....Sep 16

Air Cdre J B Osborne *(from 260418)*

Head of Policy and Resources...N/D

Head of Contracts ....Steve Hodson

Director International Security Policy ....Nick Gurr

Head Euro-Atlantic Security Policy..Giles Ahern

Head Wider Europe Policy..N/D

Head European Bilateral Relations & EU Exit ....Linda Dann .... Aug 16

Head European Bilateral Relations & EU Exit -
 Sovereign Base Areas ....N/D

Director Judicial Engagement Policy...Peter Ryan .... Aug 09

Head Inquests, Judicial Reviews and Public Inquiries...............N/D

Head Claims and Disclosure Unit..N/D

Head Legal Policy..N/D

Director Strategic Planning...Will Jessett

Head Defence Strategy and Priorities ....Paul Wyatt

Head Cyber and Space Policy..Nick Ayling ....Apr 16

Head Global Issues ....N/D

Director Chilcot Implementation ....Roger Hutton

Director Prosperity and International Business............................Huw Walters

Head Export Policy..Vacant

Head Industrial Policy ....Vacant

Head Defence Investment Security Team ....N/D

DEFENCE SAFETY AUTHORITY
Defence Safety Authority, 1st Floor, Zone 6-L, Main Building, Whitehall, London SW1A 2HB
(Email: DSA-Enquiries@mod.uk)

Director General Defence Safety Authority ....Lt Gen Richard F P Felton *CBE* ....Apr 17

 Head Defence Maritime Regulator ....Cdre Steve Pearson ....Feb 16

 Head Defence Nuclear Safety Regulator ....Paul Fyfe

Director Military Aviation Authority (MAA) ....R Adm Paul A Chivers *OBE* 081215

Director Technical and Chief Technical Officer (MAA) ....R Adm Richard C Thompson *CBE* 031016

FINANCE

Director General Finance ....Cat Little

Director Finance Strategy ....Heather Tayler

 Head Financial Management, Policy and Accounting ....N/D

 Head Finance Systems Improvement ....N/D

Director Financial Planning and Scrutiny ....Richard Jones

 Head of Defence Resources ....Annette Matton

 Head of Scrutiny ....Lois Nicholson

 Head of Defence Portfolio Approvals and Secretariat ....N/D

 Head of Single Source Advisory Team ....N/D

Director of Audit, Risk and Assurance ....Jonathan Nancekivell-Smith

 Head of Fraud Defence ....Samantha des Forges

 Group Head Internal Audit ....Michael Cole

 Chief Risk Officer ....Simon King

 Head Risk & Assurance ....N/D

Chief Commercial Officer ....Andrew Forzani

 Head Commercial HOCS ....Rachel Pearson

 Head Commercial Navy ....N/D

 Head Commercial Army ....Fiona Phillips

 Head Commercial Air ....N/D

 Head Commercial JFC ....Ian Burton

 Head ISS Commercial Operations ....Richard Jefferys

 Head Commercial Assurance, Scrutiny & Due Diligence ....Jenny Giblett

 Head Strategic Supplier Management ....Helen Sawford

 Head Policy, Process & Procedures ....Richard Marwood

HEAD OFFICE AND COMMISSIONING SERVICES

Director General Head Office & Commissioning Services ....Julie Taylor

Director Central Legal Services ....Isabel Letwin

 Sovereign Base Areas Administration Attorney General and Legal Adviser ....Stuart Howard

Director Head Office ....Alison Stevenson

 Head of Resources ....N/D

 Head Security, Safety and Business Resilience ....N/D

 Chief Security Advisor ....N/D

Director Head Office Design Programme ....Andy Helliwell

Director Change and Efficiency ....Ian Forber

Director Commissiong Services..Mark Preston

Head Defence Reform Unit and Business
Strategy & Governance...Adam Powell

Director Performance & Analysis ....Jonathan Nancekivell-Smith

Head Corporate Strategy and Governance...............................N/D

Chief Analyst ....Tony O'Connor ....Jan 17

Chief Executive Officer Defence Business Services....................Kathy Barnes

DBS Managing Director UK Security Vetting...........................Neil Watkinson

DBS Chief Operating Officer UK Security Vetting...................Jon Parkin

DBS Acting Head Veterans UK ....Rob Rowntree

DBS Head Civilian Personnel..Andrew Stafford

DBS Head Finance and Procurement Services........................Andy Dowds

DBS Chief Operating Officer ....Tamsin Woodeson

DBS Transformation Director..Jenny Sandham

DBS Chief Information Officer...Pete Bennington

DBS Head Resources...Georgina Benzies

DBS Head People Change and Development ....Ben Kinley

DBS Head Military Personnel..Brig Paul Burns

MINISTRY OF DEFENCE POLICE (MDP)
MDP HQ, Wethersfield, Braintree, Essex CM7 4AZ
Email: MDP-FOI-DP@mod.uk Tel: 01371 854000)

Chief Constable of the Minsitry of Defence Police ....Andrew Adams

Deputy Chief Constable MDP...Peter Terry QPM

Head of Resources and Progam MDP ....Justin Oliver

Assistant Chief Constable Operations..Paul McLaughlin

*Assistant Chief Constable Organisational
Development and Crime (ODC) MDP*...............................David Long

DEFENCE COMMUNICATIONS

Director Defence Communications...Carl Newns ....Jun 15

Head of Public Relations..Owen Bassett

Head of Stategy ....Brig Anthony P Duncan.......................................Sep 17

Head of Defence Communications Change Programme..............Charlie McBride ....May 15

Head of Marketing and Internal Communication ....Wendy Proctor

DEFENCE EQUIPMENT AND SUPPORT (DE&S)

Ministry of Defence, DE&S Secretariat, Maple 0a, #2043,
MOD Abbey Wood, Bristol BS34 8JH
Tel: 030 679 32222   Email: DESSec-Internet@mod.uk
Website: www.gov.uk/government/organisations/defence-equipment-and-support
Tel: 030 679 30206   Email: DESSec-ParliamentaryBusiness@mod.uk

(as of 18 May 2018)

Non-Executive Chair .... Paul Skinner *CBE*

Chief Executive .... Tony Douglas
   Chief of Staff .... Dawn Cunningham-Martin
   APS .... Linette Haines

Chief of Materiel Ships .... Sir Simon Bollom
   Military Assistant .... Cdr Pauline Aird

Chief of Materiel Submarines .... VAdm Sir Simon Lister
   Military Assistants .... Lt Cdr Laura Carter
                                                            Lt Phillip Griffith

Chief of Materiel Land .... Lt Gen Paul Jaques *CBE*
   Military Assistant .... Lt Col Paul Cummings

Chief of Materiel Air .... AM Julian A Young *CB OBE CEng FIET*
   Military Assistant .... Wg Cdr Ben Trapnell
   AMA .... Flt Lt Fergus Atkinson-O'Sullivan
   Executive Assistant .... Karen Brooker
   Chief of Staff (Air) .... Air Cdre Adam M Sansom
   Chief Financial Officer (Air) .... Heather Grossman

Chief of Materiel Joint Enablers .... Pete Worrall *CB OBE*
   Military Assistant .... Maj Simon Burkill
   Private Secretary .... Tom Hallawell

Functional Directors:

   Director General Commercial .... Nick Elliott
   Director General Resources .... Michael Bradley
   Director Human Resources .... Don Cuthbert
   Director General Programmes .... Tony Chisnall
   Director Corporate Operations .... Barry Burton

MATERIEL AIR

AIR SUPPORT

Director Air Support...Adrian Baguley
   Military Assistant ....Sqn Ldr Adam Spear
   Safety and Engineering -Team Leader...Anton Burford
   Finance - Team Leader...Robin Welham

Head of Air Transport ....Steve Horrocks
   C-17 & Command Support & Airborne Equiment - Team Leader.....Rob Pitts
   C-130J - Team Leader..Gp Capt Scott Wray

Head of A400M / Voyager..Air Cdre Stephen J Wilcock *MBE*
   A400M - Project Manager; ....James Dowson
   Voyager - SDM ....Lyndon Hoyle

Head of Air ISTAR (Information, Surveillance, Target
   Acquisition and Reconnaissance) ....Christopher Dell
   Sentry SDM.. TBA
   Sentry Capability Sustainment PM..................................Tom Pink
   Sentinal DSM..Lyn Tyacke
   Sentinal Sustainment PM ....Wg Cdr Rob Hart
   Head Airseeker Programme ....Bill Chrispin

Head of Air Systems, Equipment & Training...................Jon Haiseldon
   Aircraft Commodities - Team Leader ....Iain McLeod
   Air Platform Systems - Team Leader...............................Ian Christie (temp)
   Flight Simulation & Synthetic Trainers - Team Leader...................Russ Cole

Science Gateway..Benjamin Maddison

CHIEF OF STAFF (AIR)

Air Chief of Staff...Air Cdre Adam M Sansom
   Shared Services - Team Leader......................................Paul Mason
   Portfolio Office - Team Leader ....Henry Prag
   Special Projects...Wg Cdr Mark Robinson
   Air ILogs ....John Farrow

AIRWORTHINESS

Head of DE&S Airworthiness Team (DAT).......................Air Cdre Andy Read
   Technical - Dep Head...Alan Dukes
   Workforce & Plans - Dep Head ....N/A

COMBAT AIR

DIRECTOR COMBAT AIR ....AVM Keith H R Bethell *CBE* 040716
    Military Assistant ....Sqn Ldr Thomas McGowan
    Executive Assistant ....Karen Hall

Head of Fast Air Support Team ....Air Cdre Paul H Lloyd

Head of Lightning II ....Mark Thornton

Head of UK Military Flying Training System ....Cdre Tom Manson

Head of Unmanned Air Systems ....Air Cdre Simon D Ellard

COMBAT AIR SUPPORT TEAM

Head of Strategic Programmes ....Chris White-Horne

Head of Commercial ....Phil Tozer
    Business Support -Team Leader...Matt Rowe
    Finance - Team Leader..Adrian Morris
    Safety & Engineering - Team Leader..Gp Capt Adam Northcote-Wright
    Science Gateway ....Dr Simon Lovell
    Joint Propulsion - Team Leader ....Wally Waldron

SAFETY & ENVIRONMENT, QUALITY AND TECHNOLOGY

Director Safety & Environment, Quality and Technology ....AVM Michael Quigley
    Executive Assistant ....Kerry Lovell
    Chief of Staff...David Roberts
    Quality, Safety & Envionrmental Protection - Head........................John Allan
    Engineering Group - Head ....Clive Buckley (temp)
    Technology Office - Heaad ....Heather Goldstraw
    Science Gateway ....Dr David Guy

MATERIEL JOINT ENABLERS

HELICOPTERS

Director Helicopters..AVM Graham M Russell
    Military Assistant ....Sqn Ldr Pete McAdam
    Executive Assistant ....Lindsay Haldane-Unwin
    Finance - Team Leader ....Nick Daniels

Head Helicopters 1 ....Brig Darren Crook
    Merlin - Team Leader..Capt Kieran O'Brien *RN*
    Lynx-Wildcat - Team Leader ....Capt Mark Langrill *RN*

Head Helicopters 2 ....Ian Craddock
    Puma 2 Gazelle - Team Leader..Alan Draper *(temp)*
    Special Projects Multi Air Platform (SPMAP) - Team Leader...........Capt John Vickers *RN*

Head Helicopters 3 ....Air Cdre Owen R J Barnes *(temp)*
    Chinnook - Team Leader..Mark Geoghegan
    Apache - Team Leader ....Col Dave Potts
    Science Gateway - Team Leader...Pat Collins
    Safety - Team Leader ....Gareth Rudge
    Helicopters Business Transformation ....John Taylor

Head Helicopters Commercial..Anne Huckle

ISTAR

Director ISTAR ....Dr Simon Dakin
    Military Assistant ....Maj Luke Campbell
    Executive Assistant ....Ann-Marie Crampton
    Finance - Team Leader..Andrew Hart

ISTAR Commercial - Head ....Doug Price

ISTAR Programme Delivery Group 2 - Head ....Ian Smith
    Chemical Biological Radiologial and
        Nuclear Protection (CBRN) - Team Leader................................Ian Matthews
    Special Projects - Communications and Force Protection
        (SP CRP) - Team Leader...Vikash Patel
    Special Projects - Information Surveillance Reconnaissance
        (SPISR) - Team Leader..Mark Nileshwar
    Special Projects - Information Systems and Network
        (SPISN) - Team Leader..Paul Russell

ISTAR Programme Delivery Group 3 - Head ....Chris Carpenter
    Situational Awareness Command &
        Control (SACC) Delivery Team - Team Leader ....Adam Mehers

Marshall - Team Leader ....Mick Browm

Air Defence & Electronic Warfare Systems - Team Leader ....Dave Braun

Joint Sensor & Engagement Networks - Team Leader ....Steve Wyatt

Windfarm - Team Leader ....Chris Parker

ISTAR Business Management Team - Team Leader ....Mark Grinnall

ISTAR Science Gateway...Darren Watts

DISPOSAL SERVICES AUTHORITY (DSA)

DSA, Defence Equipment & Support (DE&S), Building H9, Ploughley Road,
Lower Arncott, Bicester, Oxon OX25 2LD
(Tel: 030 6770 2911   Email: DESLCSLS-edisposals@mod.uk)

Head Defence Equipment Sales Authority (DESA) ....Clive Walker

Commmerical Disposals Deputy Head (Bichester) ....Sara King

Captial Equipment Sales TL..Lee Nicholls

BRITISH FORCES POST OFFICE

HQ BFPO, West End Road, Ruislip, Middlesex HA4 6DQ
(Tel: +44 (0)345 769 7978   Email: DESBFPO-enquiries@mod.uk
Website: www.gov.uk/bfpo)

Head of BFPO...Col Andrew Moffat *OBE*

DEFENCE INFRASTRUCTURE ORGANISATION (DIO)

DIO Headquarters, Kingston Road, Sutton Coldfield, West Midlands B75 7RL
(Tel: 0121 311 2140   Email: DIOSEC-GroupMailbox@mod.uk
Website: www.gov.uk/government/organisations/defence-infrastructure-organisation)

(as of March 18)

Chief Executive..Graham Dalton..101016

Chief of Staff...Lucy Bogue...Aug 17

Director Commmercial ....Sean Balmer *(until Dec 17)*
                                                       Jacqui McGowan *(from Dec 17)*

Head Business Assurance & Risk ....Gordon Kennedy..Sep 14

Head Strategic Stakeholder Engagement & Comms ....James Colman..Jan 15

Chief Operating Officer ....Geoff Robson

Director Service Delivery...Richard McKinney

Head Service Delivery - Accommodation ....Air Cdre I R Tolfts OBE *(until 020418)*
                                                       Air Cdre W Rothery *(from 020418)*

Head Service Delivery - Coherence & Plans...........................Jon Powell..Jan 16

Head Service Deilvery - Training...................................N/D

Head Unarmed Guarding...N/D

Head Future Procurement Group......................................N/D

Head Service Delivery - Total Facilities Management ....N/D

Head Energy, Utilities & Sustainability...........................N/D

Director Strategic Asset Management...............................Maj Gen Nick Cavanagh

Head of Estates..Robert Stone ....Sep 16

Head Estate Strategy...Francesca Fryer...Feb 12

Head Estate Commercialisation......................................Colin Dabin...Sep 17

Head Safety, Environment & Engineering ....Sean McGovern

Director Special Projects ....Sean Balmer...Dec 17

Director Project & Programme Delivery...............................Tony Gaiani *(until Oct 17)*
                                                       John McGowan *(from Oct 17)*

Head Project & Programme Delivery - Projects ....David Salmond ....Mar 17

Head Army Basing Programme...Mark Duddy

Director Clyde Programme ....Ed Welsh

Director Data Analytics & Insight ....Tony Gosling

Head Data Analytics & Insight ....Ian Wallis..Sep 14

Director Asset Strategy & Portfolio................................Craig Cooper

Director of Finance ....Iain Sale *(until Dec 17)*
                                                       Kate Harrison *(from Apr 18)*

Director Transformation & Change ....Nik Doyle

Director Human Resources ....Helen Hall

Head Portfolio Management Office ....Vacant

Deputy Director Transformation & Change ....Vacant

31

JOINT FORCES COMMAND (JFC)

JFC HQ, Joint Headquarters Building 410, Northwood Headquarters,
Sandy Lane, Northwood, Middlesex HA6 3HP

Commander JFC	Gen *Sir* Christopher M Deverell *KCB MBE*	
	ADC Gen	Apr 16
Assistant Chief Defence Staff (Logistics Operations)	Maj Gen Angus S J Fay *CB*	Nov 14
Head Defence Logistic Operations and Capability	Air Cdre Richard Hill	Sep 17
Head Defence Logistic Policy	Air Cdre Damian R Alexander *CBE (until May 17)*	
Head Defence Logistics Strategy	Cdre Adrian Aplin	
Director Capability	Maj Gen John R Patterson *(until Apr 18)*	Oct 14
	R Adm James D Morley *(from Apr 18)*	
Head of Capability C4ISR	Air Cdre Nicholas J Hay *OBE*	Jan 16
Head of Capability Special Projects	Brig Robin Anderton-Brown	
Director Resources and Policy	Andy Helliwell *(until Jun 17)*	
Deputy Director Policy	N/D	
Deputy Director Resources	N/D	
Deputy Director Programmes	Air Cdre Andrew H Steele	Apr 17
Head of Infrastructure	Brig J Crawford	

PERMANENT JOINT HEADQUARTERS (PJHQ)

PJHQ, Sandy Lane, Northwood, Middlesex HA6 3AP

Chief of Joint Operations	Vice Admiral Timothy Fraser *CB*	Jun 17
Chief of Staff (Operations)	AVM Gary M Waterfall *CBE (until Jun 17)*	May 16
Assistant Chief of Staff Personnel Admin & Logistics (J1 J4)	Cdre Richard A Murrison *(until Apr 18)*	Aug 15
	Air Cdre Richard D Pratley *(from Apr 18)*	
Assistant Chief of Staff Intelligence (J2)	Brig Nicholas A Baker	Apr 16
Assistant Chief of Staff Operations (J3)	Brig Colin R J Weir *DSO MBE (until Apr 19)*	Apr 17
Assistant Chief of Staff Policy & Plans (J5)	Air Cdre Justin S Reuter *(until Sep 18)*	Sep 16
	Brig Charles S Collins *(from Sep 18)*	
Assistant Chief of Staff Communications (J6)	Air Cdre Nicholas J Lloyd	Dec 16
Chief of Staff (Policy & Finance)	Paul Wyatt	
Assistant Chief of Staff Policy, Legal & Media Ops (J9)	N/D	
Assistant Chief of Finance & Civilian Support to Operations (J8)	N/D	

No 83 Expeditionary Air Group (83 EAG)
RAF Al Udeid, Qatar
(Headquarrters of UK Air Component Commander)

Air Officer Commanding (AOC) and UK Air Component Commander	Air Cdre Roderick J Dennis *OBE (until Oct 18)*	Oct 17
Expeditionary Air Wings (EAW)		
Deputy Air Component Commander and Commanding Officer 901 EAW, RAF Al Udeid,Qatar	N/D	
Commanding Officer 902 EAW, RAFO Musannah, Oman	N/D	
Commanding Officer 903 EAW, RAF Akrotiri, Cyprus	Gp Capt Mike J Blackburn	240616
Commanding Officer 906 EAW, Al Minhad Air Base, UAE (UK Air Mobility Hub)	N/D	

JOINT COMMANDS AND OVERSEAS SUPPORT (JCOS) TEAM

JCOS, Joint Forces Command, Northwood Headquarters, Northwood, Middlesex HA6 3HP

PERMANENT JOINT OPERATING BASES (PJOBs)

Joint Commands and Overseas Support, Joint Forces Command,
Sandy Lane, Northwood, Middlesex HA6 3AP

Chief of Staff ....R Adm Tony Radakin *(until Mar 18)* ....Jan 16

AVM John J Stringer *(from Mar 18)*

BRITISH FORCES CYPRUS
HQ British Forces Cyprus, BFPO 53

Commander ....Maj Gen James T E Illingworth *OBE* ....Feb 17

Chief of Staff British Forces Cyprus ....Air Cdre Suzanne N Perkins...............................Aug 17

BRITISH FORCES GIBRALTAR
HQ British Forces Gibraltar, BFPO 52

Commander ....Cdre Michael J D Walliker *OBE RN* ....Jul 16

BRITISH FORCES SOUTH ATLANTIC ISLANDS
HQ British Forces South Atlantic Islands, BFPO 655

(Based at: Mount Pleasant Airfield, Falkland Islands)

Commander ....Brig Barry W Bennett ....Apr 17

BRITISH FORCES BRITISH INDIAN OCEAN TERRITORIES
HQ British Forces British Indian Ocean Territories, BFPO 485

(Based at: Diego Garcia Island)

Commander ....Cdr Karen Cahill *RN*

JOINT FORCE DEVELOPMENT

Director Joint Force Development ....V Adm Duncan L Potts *CB (until Apr 18)* ....Sep 14

AM Edward J Stringer *CBE (from Apr 18)*

Director Joint Warfare ....AVM Bruce H Hedley *MBE ADC MA*................May 16

Deputy Director Joint Warfare...Air Cdre Stephen E Reeves ....Jun 16

Commander Joint Air Land Organisation.................................Brig Henry F S Nickerson ....Apr 15

STANDING JOINT FORCE HQ (SJFHQ)

Commander ....Maj Gen Stuart Skeates *CBE (until 2018)*

Maj Gen Douglas M Chalmers *(from 2018)*

Chief of Staff Standing Joint Force Command...........................Brig Matthew J Holmes *RM (until Apr 18)* ....Apr 16

Chief of Joint Force Operations..Brig John H Ridge ....Sep 17

Commander Joint Force Logistics Component...........................Cdre Andrew J Kyte *(until Nov 18)* ....Sep 17

Brig Simon W Holford *(from Nov 18)*

DEFENCE ACADEMY OF THE UNITED KINGDOM (DEFAC)

Shrivenham, Wiltshire SN6 8LA
(Tel: 01793 314828   Website: www.da.mod.uk)

Defence Academy Operations Director ....Mark Alexander ....Dec 15

Head of Corporate Services ....Steve Petrie

TECHNOLOGY SCHOOL
Defence Academy of the United Kingdom, Shrivenham, Swindon SN6 8LA
(Tel: 01793 314828 Email: admin.hq@da.mod.uk)

Head of Technology School ....Dr Matt Chinn

Defence Capability Centre (DCC)
Defence Academy of the United Kingdom, Shrivenham, Swindon SN6 8LA

BUSINESS SKILLS COLLEGE (BSC)
Defence Academy of the United Kingdom, Shrivenham, Swindon SN6 8LA
(Tel: 01793 314828 Email: info@da.mod.uk)

Head of Business Skills College .... Claudia Luca ....Apr 17

NUCLEAR DEPARTMENT (ND)
HMS Sultan, Military Road, Gosport, Hampshire PO12 3BY
(Tel: 02392 542260   Email: info@da.mod.uk)

Head of Defence Academy Nuclear Department ....Prof Clare M Scudder

SHRIVENHAM LEADERSHIP CENTRE (SLC)
Shrivenham SN6 8LA , UK
(Tel: 01793 314828 Email: info@da.mod.uk)

ARMED FORCES CHAPLAINCY CENTRE (AFCC)
AFCC, Amport House, Amport, Andover, Hampshire SP11 8BG

DEFENCE CENTRE OF TRAINING SUPPORT (DCTS)
Kermode Hall, RAF Halton, Aylesbury, Buckinghamshire HP22 5PG

WELBECK DEFENCE SIXTH FORM COLLEGE
Forest Road, Woodhouse, Loughborough, Leicestershire, LE12 8WD
(Tel: 01509 891700   Email: helpdesk@dsfc.ac.uk   Website: www.dsfc.ac.uk)

Principal ....Mr J Peter Middleton *MA*

Director of Operations ....Lt Col (Retd) Richard Spiby *MA BA*

Military Staff:

Vice Principal Military ....Maj Jules Swindells *MSc BEng*

Training Officer ....Flt Lt Jon-Paul Priest

Adjutant ....Flt Lt Pete Smith

College Sergeant Major (CSM)...WO2 Paul Derbyshire

Military Administrator..Mr Daniel Adkin

ROYAL COLLEGE OF DEFENCE STUDIES (RCDS)
RCDS, Belgrave Square, 37 Upper Belgrave St., London SW1X 8NS

Commandant ....*Sir* Tom R V Phillips *KCMG* ....Sep 14

Deputy Commandant & Senior Directing Staff (A) ....R Adm John M L Kingwell *CBE* ....May 16

Senior Directing Staff (Air) ....Air Cdre John Philliban ....Oct 17

Senior Directing Staff (B)..Jeremy Jarvis

Senior Directing Staff (C)..James Kidner

Senior Directing Staff (D)..Maj Gen (Retd) Simon Porter..............................Apr 14

JOINT SERVICES COMMAND AND STAFF COLLEGE (JSCSC)
Faringdon Road, Shrivenham, Swindon SN6 8TS
(Tel: 01793 788000 Email: infodesk.jscsc@defenceacademy.mod.uk)

Commandant	AVM Christopher J Luck *MBE*	Feb 17
Deputy Commandant	Cdre Jeremy J F Blunden *CBE LVO*	Jun 16
Assistant Commandant (Maritime)	Cdre Jeremy J F Blunden *CBE LVO*	Jun 15
Assistant Commandant (Land)	Brig Andrew M Roe	Aug 17
Assistant Commandant (Air)	Air Cdre Scott M Miller	Nov 16
Director Army Division	Brig Edward J R Chamberlain *(until Aug 18)*	Aug 15

SURGEON GENERAL
HQ Surgeon General, Coltman House, DMS Whittington, Lichfield Barracks,
Whittington, Lichfield, Staffordshire WS14 9PY

Surgeon General	Surg R Adm Alasdair Walker *OBE QHS*	Dec 15
Director Healthcare Delivery and Training	AVM *The Hon* Richard Broadbridge *QHS*	191214
Commander Defence Medical Group	Surg Cdre Andrew S Hughes *QHP (until Sep 18)*	
Commander Defence Primary Healthcare	Surg Cdre Paul Hughes *QHP (until Jan 18)*	
Head of Healthcare Education and Training	Brig Robin Simpson	
Head of Future Healthcare	Air Cdre Maria M Byford	
Director Medical Policy and Operational Capability	Maj Gen Martin C M Bricknell *QHP*	141215
Head of Medical Policy and Information Systems	Air Cdre Alastair N Reid *QHP*	Jun 16
Medical Director	Air Cdre Richard Withnall *QHS*	Sep 17
Head of Medical Operational Capability	Surg Cdre Stuart Millar *QHS*	
Inspector General	Air Cdre D C McLoughlin *OBE*	270317
Head Strategy Planning & Business Management	N/D	
Head of Secretariat & Finance	Rich Wallace	Feb 18

DEFENCE INTELLIGENCE

Chief of Defence Intelligence	AM Philip C Osborn *CBE*	Jan 15
Deputy Chief of Defence Intelligence	Paul Rimmer	
Head of Defence Intelligence Strategic Assessments	N/D	
Head of Defence Intelligence Capability Assessments	N/D	
Head of Defence Intelligence Resources	N/D	
Head of Defence Intelligence Counter-Proliferation	N/D	
Head of Defence Intelligence Operations	Air Cdre Michael P Hart *(until Jan 18)*	Aug 15
Head of Joint Terrorism Analysis Centre	AVM Michael P Hart	Jan 18
Director Cyber, Intelligence, Surveillance and Reconnaissance	Air Cdre Ian F Vallely *OBE*	Feb 18
Head of C4ISR Joint User	Air Cdre Nicholas J Hay *OBE (until Feb 18)*	Jan 16
	Air Cdre Timothy D Neal-Hopes *(from Feb 18)*	
Commander Joint Cyber and Electromagnetic Activity Group	Air Cdre Ian F Vallely *OBE (until Apr 18)*	050116
	Brig Mark C Proctor *(from Apr 18)*	
Commander Joint Forces Intelligence Group	Brig Ben A Kite *OBE (until Dec 18)*	May 16
Head of Defence Intelligence Counter-Intelligence	N/D	
Deputy Director Military Support, JSSU Cheltenham	Air Cdre Nigel J Colman *OBE*	Jul 15

JOINT FORCES INTELLIGENCE GROUP (JFIG)
RAF Wyton, Wyton Airfield, Huntingdon, Cambridgeshire PE28 2EA (Tel: 01480 52451)

Commander JFIG	Brig Benedict Kite	May 16

Defence Geographic Centre (DGC)
Bomford Building, Elmwood Avenue, Feltham, Middlesex TW13 7AH (Tel: 020 8818 2180)

Director	Ian Spencer	Oct 15

Defence Intelligence Fusion Centre (DIFC)
RAF Wyton, Wyton Airfield, Huntingdon, Cambridgeshire PE28 2EA (Tel: 01480 52451)
Director..Gp Capt Andrew E Stewart...............................Aug 15

Joint Services Signals Organisation (JSSO) - RAF Digby, Lincoln, Lincolnshire LN4 3LH

Joint Intelligence Training Group (JITG)
Chicksands, Shefford, Bedfordshire SG17 5PR
Commander...Gp Capt Stuart Stirrat..Jun 15

DEVELOPMENT CONCEPTS AND DOCTRINE CENTRE (DCDC)
Ministry of Defence Shrivenham , SWINDON, Wiltshire SN6 8RF
(Tel: 01793 31 4216/4217/4220   Mil: 96161 4216/4217/4220   Email: DCDC-DocEds@mod.gov.uk)

Director ....Maj Gen Gerald I Mitchell *MBE* ....Apr 16
Head of Doctrine, Air and Space ....Air Cdre Neil W G Laird *CBE (until Mar 18)*.........Jul 14
                                                                                 Air Cdre P T G Lester *(from Mar 18)*
Head of Concepts and Land ....Brig Darrell P Amison *CBE (until Sep 18)* ....Sep 15
Head of Futures and Strategy ....Brig Ewen Murchison *RM* ....Dec 17

INFORMATION SYSTEMS AND SERVICES (ISS)

ISS Chief Executive Officer.......................................Lt Gen Ivan Hooper...Apr 14
ISS Defence as a Platform Portfolio Director............Jim Knight *OBE*...Sep 17
ISS Chief Information Officer.....................................Brig Scott R Workman *(until Jul 18)*....................Apr 13
ISS Head of Finance ....Naina Burgess
ISS Head of People Change ....Vacant
ISS Chief Operating Officer.......................................Brig Graham W Fletcher *(from Jul 18)*
ISS Director Service Operations ....Lt Gen I Hooper *(until Feb 18)*
                                                                                 AVM Christopher J Moore *(from Feb 18)*
ISS Head of Customer Services.................................Brig Charles S Maconochie ....Sep 16
ISS Head of Operate and Defend..............................Capt Shaun Prescott *RN*
ISS Head of Service Performance..............................Mike Roden
ISS Director Service Development ....David Lynam *MBE* ....Jan 15
ISS Head of Networks ....Brig Mike Griffiths
ISS Head of BATCIS...Brig Richard Spencer *(until May 18)*
ISS Head of SANGCOM Programme Director ....Brig Peter Drew
ISS Head of Deployed Systems..................................Brig Frederick E Hargreaves ....Jan 17
ISS Head of Application Services and Development Operations...Brig Sara L Sharkey.................................Apr 17
ISS Head of Intelligence Systems ....Richard Bloomfield
ISS Head of Portfolio Management Office..................Jim Robinson
ISS Head of Security Infrastructure ....Dave Medwell
ISS Head of New Style of IT and Integrated User Services ....Gareth Clark
ISS Head of Defence as a Platform............................Itendra Tiwari
ISS Director Service Design ....Martin C Elliot..Jun 16
ISS Head Strategy ....Air Cdre David J Rowland....................................Nov 16
ISS Design Chief Operating Officer...........................Claire Fry
ISS MOD Information Head of Profession ....Ian Henderson
ISS Head of Corporate and Management Information..................Natalie Wirth
ISS Head of Defence Assurance and Information Security...........John Cook
ISS Chief Architect...Steve Latchem
ISS Head of Innovation Strategy...............................Danny Wootton
ISS Head of Innovation Realisation...........................Mike Feltham
ISS Head Customer Relationship Management............Col Justin Hodges
ISS Director Commercial..Rob Lees
ISS Head of Commerical Transformation.....................Ian Adam
ISS Head of Defence as a Platform Commercial.........Dave Anderson
ISS Head of Commerical...Richard Jefferys

MOD EXECUTIVE AGENCIES

DEFENCE ELECTRONICS AND COMPONENTS AGENCY

Welsh Road, Deeside, Flintshire CH5 2LS (Tel: 01244 847745 Email: decainfo@deca.mod.uk
Website: www.gov.uk/government/organisations/defence-electronics-and-components-agency)
(Source: Annual report and accounts 2016/2017, July 2017)

DECA Board

Independent non-executive chairman	Alex Jablonowski
Non-executive directors	Peter Short
	Tim Walton

Executive Management Board

Chief Executive	Geraint Spearing
Finance Director	Lin Longman
Head of Strategy, Governance & Secretariat	Jason Leeks
Support Services Director	Ian Doughty
Operations Director	Wayne Baker
Commercial Director	Keith Pavett
Business Development Director	Ian Cole

DEFENCE SCIENCE AND TECHNOLOGY LABORATORY (DSTL)

DSTL Headquarters, Porton Down, Salisbury, Wilts SP4 0JQ
(Tel: 01980 950000 (central enquiries)   Email: centralenquiries@dstl.gov.uk
Website: www.gov.uk/government/organisations/defence-science-and-technology-laboratory)

Chairman	*Sir* David Pepper *KCMG*	010814
Chief Executive	Gary Aitkenhead	Dec 17
Independent Non-Executive Directors	Sir David Grant *CBE*	010612
	Jeremy Monroe	010217
	David Tonkin	Sep 17
Non-Executive Director	Mark Preston	020516
Technology Director	Dr Bryn Hughes	011015
Capability and Delivery Director	David Marsh	180416
Finance Director	David English	010416
Infrastructure Director	Graham Balmer	
People and Business Services Director	Joanne Peel	250116

DEFENCE AND SECURITY ACCELERATOR

GO1, Building 5, Porton Down, Salisbury, Wiltshire SP4 0JQ
(Email: accelerator@dstl.gov.uk   Tel: +44 (0)1980 950000 option 3)

Head of the Defence and Security Accelerator	Dr Lucy Mason

UK HYDROGRAPHIC OFFICE (UKHO)

UKHO, Admiralty Way, Taunton, Somerset TA1 2DN
(Tel: +44 (0)1823 484444   Email: customerservices@ukho.gov.uk   Website: www.gov.uk/ukho)

Non-Executive Chair	Adam Singer
Chief Executive	John Humphrey
National Hydrographer and Deputy Chief Executive	R Adm Tim M Lowe *CBE* .... Aug 15
Director of Corpoerate Services	Peter Davis *OBE*
Non-Executive Directors	Marion Leslie
	Heather Tayler
	Alison Henwood
	Tom Loosemore
Captain HM and Hydrographer of the Navy	Capt Gary Hesling

HER MAJESTY'S NAUTICAL ALMANAC OFFICE

UK Hydrographic Office, Admiralty Way, Taunton TA1 2DN
(Tel: +44 (0)1823 4844444   Email: hmnao@ukho.gov.uk   Website: http://astro.ukho.gov.uk/nao/)

Head ....Dr Steve A Bell

OFFICE OF THE JUDGE ADVOCATE GENERAL (OJAG)

9th Floor, Thomas More Building, The Royal Courts of Justice, The Strand, London WC2A 2LL
(Tel: 020 7013 1618   Fax: 0870 3240044   Email: Ben.Yallop@judiciary.gsi.gov.uk)

(correct as of 19 Jun 17)

Judge Advocate General	His Honour Judge Blackett	281004
Vice-Judge Advocate General	Judge Michael Hunter	010184
Assistant Judge Advocate General	Judge Camp	180488
	Judge McGrigor	031005
	Judge Hill	101005
	Judge Large	010110
Head of Office	Ben Yallop	
Administrator	Marie Bantoft	

THE MILITARY COURT SERVICE

Building 398, Trenchard Lines, Upavon, Pewsey, Wilts SN9 6BE
(Tel: 01980 618058   Fax: 01980 618060   Email: mcs-group@mod.uk)

Military Court Centres:

Bulford (Wilts)
Catterick (Yorks)
Colchester (Essex)
Portsmouth (Hants)

Aldergrove (Northern Ireland)
Sennelager (Germany)
Episkopi (Cyprus)

SERVICE PROSECUTING AUTHORITY (SPA)

Address: RAF Northolt, West End Road, Ruislip, Middlesex, HA4 6NG
Tel: 020 8842 6105   Email: SPA-Media@mod.uk   Website: spa.independent.gov.uk)

Director Service Prosecutions (DSP)...Mr Andrew Cayley *CMG QC*...........................03 Dec 13
Deputy Director Service Prosecutions (DDSP)...............................Mr Darren Reed

SOVEREIGN BASE AREAS OF
AKROTIRI AND DHEKELIA ADMINISTRATION

Headquarters, Sovereign Base Areas Administration, Episkopi,
British Forces Post Office 53
Website: www.sbaadministration.org

Administrator and Commander
British Forces Cyprus (BFC) .... Maj Gen James T E Illingworth *OBE* .....Feb 17

Deputy Administrator .... Air Cdre Suzanne N Perkins

Chief Officer, Sovereign Base Area (SBA) Administration .... Mr Michael John Smith 020117

Attorney General Legal Advisor (AGLA Office)
Attorney General and Legal Adviser .... Mr Stuart David Howard 170916

Judiciary
The Resident Judges' Court
Resident Judge .... His Honour Judge Raymond H Naqvi
TD (until 2017)

The Senior Judges' Court
Presiding Judge .... His Honour Judge Timothy Clayson

Senior Judges
His Honour Judge Robert Juckes *QC* .... 17 Jan 14 - 16 Jan 19
His Honour Judge Robert W Fraser *MVO* .... 14 Jun 14 - 13 Jun 19
His Honour Judge Mark Bishop .... 01 Dec 16 - 30 Nov 21
Her Honour Judge Janet Waddicor .... 01 Dec 16 - 30 Nov 21
Her Honour Judge Alice Robinson .... 23 Apr 17 - 23 Apr 22
His Honour Judge Colin R Burn .... 23 Apr 17 - 23 Apr 22

Associate Judges
Her Honour Judge Julie Whitby
His Honour Judge Theo C Karamanis
Her Honour Judge Tan Ilram
His Honour Judge Thomas Edward Crowther

Senior Registrar
Mrs Andri Georgiou-Antoniou 010318

SBA Police Service
Chief Constable and Superindentent of SBA Prison, Dhekelia .... Mr Chris Eyre *QPM MSA* 250716

Deputy Chief Constable .... Mr Murray Duffin

Customs and Immigration
Fiscal Officer *(acting)* .... Mr Andrew Clive Reed 130817

Deputy Fiscal Officer .... Mr Huw Griffiths

Administration
SBA Policy secretary .... Mr Paul J Newbegin 280816

Civil Secretary .... Mr Philip Leonard Mallin 171017

DEFENCE AND AIR ATTACHÉS TO BRITISH EMBASSIES

Includes non residential accreditations (NRAs). Listings correct as of March 2018.

ABU DHABI (UAE) — (British Embassy, Khalid bin Al Waleed St (Street 22), PO Box 248 Abu Dhabi, United Arab Emirates
Tel: +971 2 610 1100)

Defence Attaché	Capt Jim Lowther *RN*	Sep 17 / Sep 20
Air Attaché	Wg Cdr Nigel Cookson	Mar 17 / Mar 20

British Defence Staff (BDS-G) - Lodged in Dubai, UAE

British Defence Staff Gulf Chief of Staff	Col Tom Ridgway
British Defence Staff Gulf SO1	Wg Cdr Angela Graham
British Defence Staff Gulf SO2	Maj Imran Ahsan

ADDIS ABABA (ETHIOPIA) — (British Embassy, Comoros Street, Addis Ababa, 858, Ethiopia
Email: Britishembassy.addisababa@fco.gov.uk   Tel: +251 11 6170100)

Defence section resident in Addis Ababa with NRAs to Djibouti (Djibouti), Somaliland, and African Union.

Defence Attaché	Col Matt Munro	Sep 17 /

ALGIERS (ALGERIA) — (British Embassy, Ambassade Britannique, 3 Chemin Capitaine Hocine Slimane
(ex Chemin des Glycines), Algiers, Algeria
Email: BritishEmbassy.Algiers@fco.gov.uk   Tel: +213 (0) 770 085 000)

Defence section resident in Algiers with NRA to Tunisia (Tunis) resident in Algiers.

Defence Attaché	Lt Col James McLaren *OBE RM*	Jul 17 / Jul 20

ASTANA (KAZAKHSTAN) — (British Embassy, 62 Kosmonavtov Str., Renco Building, 6 Floor, Astana, 010000, Kazakhstan
Email: ukinkz@fco.gov.uk   Tel: +7 (7172) 556200)

Defence section resident in Astana with NRAs to Kyrgyzstan (Bishkek) and Tajikistan (Dushanbe).

Defence Attaché	Lt Col Andrew Houlton	Aug 17 / Aug 20

AMMAN (JORDAN) — (British Embassy, (PO Box 87) Abdoun, 11118 Amman,Jordan
Email: Amman.enquiries@fco.gov.uk   Tel: +962 (6) 590 9200)

Defence and Military Attaché	Col Hedley Tomlyn	Sep 16 / Sep 19
Naval and Air Attaché	Wg Cdr Sandy Sandilands *RAF*	Apr 17/ Apr 20

ANKARA (TURKEY) — (British Embassy, Şehit Ersan Caddesi 46/A, Çankaya, Ankara,Turkey
Email: info.officer@fco.gov.uk   Tel: +90 312 455 33 44)

Defence and Military Attaché	Col Christopher (Toffer) Beattie	Jul 15 / Jul 18
Naval and Air Attaché	Wg Cdr Bryan Hunt	Jun 15 / Jun 18

ATHENS (GREECE) — (British Embassy, 1, Ploutarchou str, 106 75 Athens, Greece
Email: information.athens@fco.gov.uk   Tel: +30 210 7272 600)

Defence section resident in Athens with NRA to Bulgaria (Sofia).

Defence and Military Attaché	Capt Tim Ferns *RN*	Jan 18 / Jan 21

BAGHDAD (IRAQ) — (British Embassy, International Zone, Baghdad, Iraq)

Defence Attaché	Brig Robert Jefferies	Jan 18 / Jan 20
Deputy Defence Attaché	Wg Cdr Jennifer Robinson	May 17 / Nov 18

BANGKOK (THAILAND) — (British Embassy, 14 Wireless Road, Lumpini, Pathumwan, Bangkok 10330, Thailand
Email: Info.Bangkok@fco.gov.uk   Tel: +66 (0) 2 305 8333)

Defence Attaché ....Col Roger Lewis .... Nov 17 / Nov 20

BEIJING (CHINA) — (British Embassy, 11 Guang Hua Lu, Jian Guo Men Wai, 100600 Beijing, China
Tel:+86 (0) 10 5192 4000)

Defence section resident in Beijing with NRA to Mongolia (Ulaanbaatar) and North Korea.

Defence and Military Attaché ....Cdre Rupert Hollins *RN* .... Aug 16 / Jul 19

Deputy Defence, Naval and Air Attaché ....Gp Capt Mike Lavendar *OBE RAF* .... Nov 15 / Jun 19

Assistant Military Attaché ....Maj Matt Hayward ....Jul 15 / Jul 18

BEIRUT (LEBANON) — (British Embassy, Serail Hill, Embassy complex, Beirut Central District, PO Box :11- 471 Beirut, Lebanon
Email: consular.beirut@fco.gov.uk   Tel: +961 (0)1 960800)

Defence Attaché ....Lt Col Chris Gunning..Apr 15/ Apr 18

Assistant Defence Attaché ....WO Tim Peggs *RAF*.. Mar 18 /

Assistant Defence Attaché, Damascus ....Sgt Joe Wilkinson ....Mar 17 / Mar 20

BELGRADE (SERBIA) — (British Embassy, Resavska 46, Belgrade, 11000, Serbia
Email: Belgrade.PPD@fco.gov.uk   Tel: +381 (11) 3060 900)

Defence Attaché ....Lt Col Simon P (Fitz) Fitzgibbon .... Mar 15 / Apr 18

BERLIN (GERMANY) — (British Embassy, Wilhelmstraße 70/71, 10117 Berlin, Germany
Email: ukingermany@fco.gov.uk   Tel: +49 (0) 30 204 570)

Defence Attaché ....Brig Robert Rider...Feb 15 / Jul 20

Naval Attaché ....Capt Andy Ewen *RN* .... Aug 17 / Aug 20

Military Attaché ....Col David Moreton ....Apr 17 / Nov 20

Air Attaché ....Gp Capt Roland Smith *OBE* ....Jul 12 / Aug 18

BOGOTA (COLOMBIA) — (British Embassy, Carrera 9, No 76-49, Piso 8, Edificio ING Barings, Bogotá, Colombia
Email: embajadabritanica.bogota@fco.gov.uk   Tel: (57) (1) 326 8300)

Defence section resident in Bogota with NRAs to Peru (Lima), Venezuela (Caracas).

Defence Attaché ....Col Jonathan P S Wright ....Jul 14 / Jul 17

Deputy Defence Attaché...Lt Cdr Aleesha Mitchell *RN*...................................Mar 18 / Mar 21

BRASILIA (BRAZIL) — (British Embassy, Quadra 801 - Conjunto K - Lote 08, CEP 70408-900 Av. das Nações - Asa Sul
Brasilia, Brazil
Email: brazil.consulate@fco.gov.uk   Tel: 55 11 3094 2700)

Defence Attaché ....Capt Kevin Fleming.. Aug 16 /

BUCHAREST (ROMANIA) — (British Embassy, 24 Jules Michelet, 010463 Bucharest, Romania
Email: BritishEmbassy.Bucharest@fco.gov.uk   Tel: +40 (21) 201 7200)

Defence Attaché ....Cdr Neville McNally *RN* .... Mar 17 / Apr 20

BUENOS AIRES (ARGENTINA) — (British Embassy, Dr Luis Agote 2412 (1425), Buenos Aires, Argentina
Email: askinformation.baires@fco.gov.uk   Tel: +54 11 4808-2200)

Defence section resident in Buenos Aires with NRAs to Uruguay (Montevideo), Paraguay (Ascuncion).

Defence Attaché ....Gp Capt Robin Smith *RAF* ....Apr 17 / Apr 20

Deputy Defence Attaché...Maj Adam Wise...Feb 17 / Feb 20

CAIRO (EGYPT) — (British Embassy, 7 Ahmed Ragheb Street, Garden City, Cairo, Egypt
Email: cairo.press@fco.gov.uk   Tel: + 2 (02) 2791 6000)

Defence and Military Attaché ....Capt Simon Ahlgren *RN*..Nov 15 / Nov 18
Deputy Defence Attaché...Lt Col Ed Sandry ....Mar 15 / Mar 18

COPENHAGEN (DENMARK) — (British Embassy, Kastelsvej 36-40, DK-2100 Copenhagen, Denmark
Email: Enquiry.Copenhagen@fco.gov.uk   Tel: +45 35 44 52 00)

Defence Attaché ....Col Sarah Johansen......................................Jan 16 / Jan 19

DAKAR (SENEGAL) — (British Embassy, 20 Rue du Dr Guillet, BP6025, Dakar, Senegal
Email: britembe@orange.sn   Tel: +221 33 823 73 92)

Defence section resident in Dakar with NRAs Defence Attaché to The Gambia (Banjul), Mali (Bamako) and Niger (Niamey).
Defence Attaché ....Lt Col Tim Mason......................................Jan 17 / Dec 19

DOHA (QATAR) — (British Embassy, West Bay, Dafna Area, Onaiza Zone 66, Al Shabab Street.,PO Box 3 Doha, Qatar
Email: Embassy.Doha@fco.gov.uk   Tel: +974 4496 2000)

Defence Attaché ....Air Cdre Patrick O'Donnell *OBE* ....Oct 17 /
Deputy Defence Attaché...Cdr Bob Bruford *RN*......................................Jan 17 /

DUBLIN (IRELAND) — (British Embassy, 29 Merrion Road, Ballsbridge, Dublin 4, Ireland
Tel: +353 (1) 205 3700)

Defence Attaché ....Col Max Walker......................................Sep 15 / Sep 18
Non Resident Naval Attaché (London)...Cdr Tim Henry
Non Resident Military Attaché (London) ....Lt Col Adrian Jones
Non Resident Air Attaché (London) ....Wg Cdr Archie McCallum *RAF*

THE HAGUE (NETHERLANDS) — (British Embassy, Lange Voorhout 10, 2514 ED The Hague, Netherlands
Email: ukinnl@fco.gov.uk   Tel: +31 (0)70 4270 427)

Defence section resident in The Hague with NRAs Defence Attaché to Belgium (Brussels) and Luxembourg.
Defence Attaché ....Col James I R Phillips......................................Jan 16 / Jan 19

HANOI (SOCIALIST REPUBLIC OF VIETNAM) — (British Embassy, Central Building, 4th floor, 31 Hai Ba Trung,
Hanoi, Vietnam. Email:generalenquiries.vietnam@fco.gov.uk
Tel: +84 (0)24 3936 0500)

Defence Attaché ....Gp Capt David Houghton ....Nov 16 / Nov 19

HARARE (ZIMBABWE) — (British Embassy, 3 Norfolk Road, Mount Pleasant, Harare, Zimbabwe
Email: ukinfo.harare@fco.gov.uk   Tel: 024 2 85855200)

Defence section resident in Harare with NRAs Defence Adviser to Malawi (Lilongwe), Botswana (Gaborone) and
Zambia (Lusaka).
Defence Attaché ....Col Mike Geldard ....Jul 17 / Jul 20

HELSINKI (FINLAND) — (British Embassy, Itäinen Puistotie 17, 00140 Helsinki, Finland
Email: Helsinki.ConsularEnquiries@fco.gov.uk   Tel: +358 (0) 9 2286 5100)

Defence Attaché ....Cdr Mark Taylor......................................Sep 16 / Sep 19

JAKARTA (INDONESIA) — (British Embassy, Jl. Patra Kuningan Raya Blok L5-6, Jakarta, 12950, Indonesia
Email: Jakarta.mcs@fco.gov.uk   Tel: (+62) (21) 2356 5200)

Defence section resident in Jakarta with NRA to Timor Leste (East Timor).
Defence Attaché ....Col Jaimie Roylance *RM* ....Sep 17 / Sep 20

JUBA (SOUTH SUDAN) — (British Embassy, EU Compound, Kololo Road, Thom Ping, Juba, South Sudan
Email: ukin.southsudan@fco.gov.uk   Tel: +211 (0) 912323712/+211 (0) 959200010)

Defence Attaché ....Lt Col Mark Hughes ....Feb 17 / Feb 19

KABUL (AFGHANISTAN) — (British Embassy, 15th St, Roundabout Wazir Akbar Khan, PO Box 334, Kabul, Afghanistan
Email: britishembassy.kabul@fco.gov.uk   Tel: +93 (0) 700 102 000)

Defence Attaché ....Col Andy Smith..Jul 17 / Jul 20

Deputy Defence Attaché...Cdr Nick Soul *RN* .... May 17 / May 19

KATHMANDU (NEPAL) — (British Embassy, PO Box 106, Lainchaur, Kathmandu, Nepal
Email: BEKathmandu@fco.gov.uk   Tel:(977) (1) 4237100)

Defence Attaché is Commander British Gurkhas Nepal and Director Gurkha Welfare Scheme.

Assistant Military Attaché is MLO British Gurkhas Nepal.

Defence Attaché ....Col Ian Logan ....Sept 15 / Jul 18

Assistant Military Attaché...Maj Dhan Bahadur Gurung.......................................Sep 15 / Sep 18

KHARTOUM (SUDAN) — (British Embassy, off Sharia Al Baladiya, Khartoum, PO Box No 801, Sudan
Tel: +249 (0)156 775500)

Defence Attaché ....Lt Col L R (Lee) Saunders.................................... Aug 16 / Aug 18

KUWAIT CITY (KUWAIT) — (British Embassy, Arabian Gulf St.,Dasman, Kuwait City, Kuwait
Tel: +965 2259 4320   Fax political & defence: +965 2259 4339)

Defense Attaché...Gp Capt Finlay McLean...Apr 16 / Jul 19

KYIV (UKRAINE) — (British Embassy, 9, Desyatynna St., Kyiv, 01901, Ukraine
Email: ukembinf@gmail.com   Tel: +380 44 490 3660)

Defence section resident in Kyiv with NRA to Republic of Moldova (Chisanau).

Defence Attaché ....Col David Warner ....Jul 17 / Ju 20

Deputy Defence Attaché...Lt Cdr Dan Hallett *RN* ....Oct 15 / May 18

LISBON (PORTUGAL) — (British Embassy, Rua de São Bernardo 33, 1249-082 Lisbon, Portugal
Email: ppa.lisbon@fco.gov.uk   Tel: +351 21 392 40 00)

Defence section resident in Lisbon with NRA to Cape Verde Islands.

Defence Attaché ....Cdr David Morgan RN...Mar 18 / Mar 21

MADRID (SPAIN)— (British Embassy, Torre Espacio, Paseo de la Castellana 259D, 28046 Madrid, Spain
Email: spain.consulate@fco.gov.uk   Tel:+34 917 146 300)

Defence Attaché ....Capt Mark Fieldsend *RN*....................................... Nov 16 / Nov 19

MEXICO CITY (MEXICO) — (British Embassy, Río Lerma, No. 71, Col. Cuauhtémoc, CP. 06500, Mexico City, Mexico
Email: ukinmexico@fco.gov.uk   Tel: +52 (55) 1670 3200)

Defence Attaché ....Capt Andy Hancock RN....................................... May 17 / May 20

Assistant Defence Attaché...CPO Jane Bouckley .... Nov 17 / Nov 20

MANAMA (BAHRAIN) — (British Embassy, 21 Government Avenue, Manama 306, P O Box 114 Manama, Bahrain
Tel:+ 973 17574100)

Defence Attaché ....Post vacant

MOGADISHU (SOMALIA) — (British Embassy Mogadishu, Mogadishu, Somalia
Email: Somalia.Enquiries@fco.gov.uk)

The defence section is lodged in Mogadishu but their support is lodged in Nairobi, Kenya.

Defence Adviser.. Lt Col Andrew Tait ....Apr 17 / Apr 19

MOSCOW (RUSSIA) — (British Embassy, 121099 Moscow, Smolenskaya Naberezhnaya 10, Russia
Tel: +7 495 956 7200   Fax (general): +7 495 956 7481)

The defence section has been reduced to an NA whose tour is scheduled to end in Sep 2018.

Defence and Air Attaché ....Post vacant

Naval Attaché ....Capt Chris Connolly *RN* ....Jun 16 / Jun 19

Assistant Naval Attaché ....Post vacant

Assistant Military Attaché..Post vacant

MUSCAT (OMAN) — (British Embassy, PO Box 185, Mina Al Fahal, 116 Muscat, Muscat, Oman
Email: muscat.enquiries@fco.gov.uk   Tel: +968 2460 9000)

Defence and Military Attaché ....Cdre Henry Duffy *RN* ....Apr 17 / Apr 20

Naval and Air Attaché...Cdr Kevin Broadley *RN* .... Aug 15 / Aug 19

OSLO (NORWAY) — (British Embassy, Thomas Heftyesgate 8, Oslo, 0244, Norway
Email: UKinNorway@fco.gov.uk   Tel: (+47) 23 13 27 00)

Defence section resident in Oslo with NRAs to Iceland (Reykjavik).

Defence Attaché ....Lt Col Andy Walker *RM* .... Aug 16 / Aug 19

PARIS (FRANCE) — (British Embassy, 35, rue du Faubourg St Honoré, Paris Cedex 08, 75383 Paris, France
Email: France.Enquiries@fco.gov.uk   Tel:+33 (0) 1 44 51 31 00)

Defence section resident in Paris with NRA to Monaco

Defence Attaché ....Brig Rob Thomson...Sep 17 / Sep 20

Deputy Defence Attachés ....Capt Keri Harris *RN*... Aug 16 / Aug 19

Col Chris Borneman ....Sep 16 / Sep 19

Gp Capt Tim Below *RAF*...Jul 17 / Sep 20

PRAGUE (CZECH REPUBLIC) — (British Embassy, Thunovska 14, 118 00, Prague, Czech Republic
Email: ukinczechrepublic@fco.gov.uk   Tel: +420 257 40 2111)

Defence section resident in Prague with NRA to Slovakia (Bratislava)

Defence Attaché...Gp Capt Mike Longstaff *OBE* ....Mar 16 / Mar 19

RABAT (MOROCCO) — (British Embassy, 28 Avenue S.A.R. Sidi Mohammed, Souissi 10105 (BP 45),, Rabat, Morocco
Email: rabat.consular@fco.gov.uk   Tel: +212 (0) 537 633 333)

Defence section resident in Rabat with NRAs Defence Attaché to Mauritania (Nouakchott).

Defence Attaché ....Lt Col Alistair Bryant...Dec 17 / Dec 20

RANGOON (BURMA) — (British Embassy, 80 Strand Road, (Box No 638), Rangoon, Burma
Tel: +95 (0) 1370865/7)

Defence Attaché ....Col R N (Nigel) Goodwin................................... Aug 16 / Aug 19

RIGA (LATVIA) — (Defence Section, British Embassy, 5, J.Alunana iela, Riga, LV 1010, Latvia
Email: britishembassy.riga@fco.gov.uk   Tel: +371 6777 4700)

Defence Attaché ....Sqn Ldr Mark Sapsford..Apr 17 / Apr 20

RIYADH (SAUDI ARABIA) — (British Embassy, PO Box 94351, 11693 Riyadh, Saudi Arabia
Email: Consular.Riyadh@fco.gov.uk   Tel: +966 (0) 11 4819 100
Fax defence: +966 (0) 11 481 9235)

Defence and Military Attaché ....Brig David Russell-Parsons *OBE* .... Oct 15 / Oct 18

Naval and Air Attaché ....Cdr Jason Horne... Jan 17 / Jan 20

ROME (ITALY) — (British Embassy, Via XX Settembre 80/a, 00187 Rome, Italy
Tel: +39 06 4220 0001)

Defence section resident in Rome with NRA to Malta.

Defence and Military Attaché ....Col Lindsay MacDuff...................................... Aug 16 / Aug 19

Naval / Air Attaché and Defence Adviser to Malta................Cdr Neil Thompson *OBE*...Apr 15 / Apr 18

SANA'S (YEMEN) — (British Embassy, /938 Thahr Himyar St., East Ring Road, near Mövenpick Hotel, Sana'a, Yemen
Tel: +44 (0)20 7008 1500)

British Embassy Sana'a has temporarily suspended operations from Wednesday 11 February 2015.
Defence section currently lodged in British Embassy Riyadh, Saudi Arabia. NRA to Eritrea (Asmara).

Defence Attaché ....Gp Capt Matt Stowers...Sep 17 / Sep 19

SANTIAGO (CHILE) — (British Embassy, Avda. El Bosque Norte 0125, Las Condes, Santiago, Chile
Email:embsan@britemb.cl   Tel: 56 2 2370 4100)

Defence Attaché ....Gp Capt Paul Warwick..Mar 16 / Mar 19

SARAJEVO (BOSNIA AND HERZEGOVINA) — (British Embassy, 39a, Hamdije Cemerlica St., 71000 Sarajevo,
Bosnia and Herzegovina
Email: britemb@bih.net.ba   Tel: +387 (0) 33 282 200)

Defence Attaché ....Lt Col Jonnie Williamson ....Sep 17 / Sep 20

SEOUL (KOREA) — (British Embassy Seoul, Sejong-daero 19-gil 24, Seoul Jung-gu, 04519, South Korea
Email: Enquiry.Seoul@fco.gov.uk   Tel: +82 (0)2 3210 5500)

Defence and Military Attaché ....Brig Huw Lloyd-Jones...Jul 16 / Jul 19

SKOPJE (MACEDONIA) — (British Embassy, Todor Aleksandrov No.165, Skopje 1000, Macedonia
Email: britishembassyskopje@fco.gov.uk   Tel: +389 (2) 3299 299)

Defence section resident in Skopje with NRAs to Kosovo (Pristina).

Defence Attaché ....Lt Col Andy Layton .... Nov 17 / Nov 20

STOCKHOLM (SWEDEN) — (British Embassy, Skarpögatan 6-8, Box 27819, 115 93 Stockholm, Sweden
Email: Stockholm@fco.gov.uk   Tel: +46 (0)8 671 30 00)

Defence Attaché..Wg Cdr Paul Lamb .... Dec 17 / Dec 20

TALLINN (ESTONIA) — (British Embassy, Wismari 6, Tallinn, 15098, Estonia
Email: infotallinn@fco.gov.uk   Tel: +372 667 4700)

Defence Attaché ....Cdr Gary Brooks *RN*... Nov 15 / Nov 18

Assistant Defence Attaché...CPO Darren Taylor .... Nov 15 / Nov 18

TASHKENT (UZBEKISTAN) — (British Embassy, 67 Gulyamov Street, Tashkent, 100000, Uzbekistan
Email: ukin.uzbekistan@fco.gov.uk   Tel: +99 871 120 1500)

Defence Attaché ....Sqn Ldr Andrew Strefford....................................... Nov 14 / Nov 17

TBILISI (GEORGIA) — (British Embassy, 51 Krtsanisi Street,Tbilisi, 0114, Georgia
Email: British.Embassy.Tbilisi@fco.gov.uk   Tel: +995 (32) 227 47 47)

Defence section resident in Tbilisi with NRAs to Armenia (Yerevan) and Azerbaijan (Baku).

Defence Attaché ....Lt Col Dave Ethell *RM* ....Sep 16 / Sep 19

Deputy Defence Attaché..Maj Will George.. Jan 18 / Jan 20

TEL AVIV (ISRAEL) — (British Embassy, 192 Hayarkon Street, 6340502 Tel Aviv, Israel,
Email: webmaster.telaviv@fco.gov.uk   Tel: +972 (0)3 725 1222)

Defence and Military Attaché ....Col Ronnie Westerman .... Jan 16 / Jan 19

Deputy Defence Attaché..Wg Cdr Tim Yates.......................................Sep 15 / Sep 18

TIRANA (ALBANIA) — (British Embassy, Rruga Skenderbeg 12, Tirana, Albania
Email: british.embassytirana@fco.gov.uk   Tel: +355 4 223 4973/4/5)

Defence section resident in Tirana with NRA to Montenegro (Podgorica).

Defence and Military Attaché ....Lt Col Edward Melotte *OBE*...................................Apr 17 / Apr 20

TOKYO (JAPAN) — (British Embassy, 102-8381, No 1 Ichiban-cho, Chiyoda-ku, Tokyo, Japan
Email: public-enquiries.tokyo@fco.gov.uk   Tel: (+81) (3) 5211-1100)

Defence section resident in Tokyo with NRA to Korea.

Defence Attaché ....Capt Paul Casson *RN* .... Aug 16 / Aug 19

Deputy Defence Attaché.......................................Maj Oli Clark .... Aug 17 / Aug 20

TRIPOLI (LIBYA)

Defence section in Tripoli has been evacuated to Tunis in Tunisia (See also entries for Tunis and Algiers)

Defence Attaché ....Capt David Robertson *RN*.....................................Mar 18 / Mar 20

TUNIS (TUNISIA)

Tunisia is served by an NRA resident in Algiers. British Embassy Tunis is host to the evacuated Defence Section Tripoli. (See also entries for Algiers and Tripoli)

UNITED NATIONS, UK Mission (New York)

Military Attaché ....Gp Capt Tim O'Brien *RAF* .... Aug 16 / Aug 19

Assitant Military Attaché ....Lt Col Andrew Norris *MBE* ....Jul 14 /Jun 17

VIENNA (AUSTRIA) — (British Embassy, Jauresgasse 12, 1030 Vienna, Austria
Email: press@britishembassy.at Tel: +43 (1) 716130)

Defence section resident in Vienna with NRA to Slovenia (Ljubljana) and Senior Military Adviser to OSCE.

Defence Attaché ....Lt Col Dean Plant...Apr 17 / Apr 20

Senior Military Adviser to OCSE........................Cdr Graham Townsend *RN* ....Dec 16 / Dec 19

VILNIUS (LITHUANIA) — (British Embassy Vilnius, Antakalnio str. 2, Vilnius, LT-10308, Lithuania
Email: Consular.Vilnius@fco.gov.uk Tel: +370 5 246 2900)

Defence Attaché ....Maj Jane Witt ....Jul 16 / Jul 19

WARSAW (POLAND) — (British Embassy, ul. Kawalerii 12, 00-468 Warsaw, mazowieckie, Poland
Email: info@britishembassy.pl   Tel: +48 22 311 00 00)

Defence, Naval and Military Attaché....................................Cdr Dominic Morgan *OBE RN* ....Feb 18 / Feb 21

WASHINGTON DC (USA) — (British Embassy, 3100 Massachusetts Avenue, NW, Washington DC 20008, USA
Tel: +1 202 588 6500)

Defence section resident in Washington DC with NRA to Bermuda (Hamilton).

Defence Attaché	AVM Gavin D A Parker *OBE RAF*	Nov 17 /
Minister (Defence Materiel)	Mr Steve McCarthy	Sep 14 / Sep 17
Military Attaché	Brig James Carr-Smith	Sep 16 / Sep 19
Naval Attaché	Cdre Martin Connell *RN*	Sep 14 / Sep 17
Air Attaché	Air Cdre James Linter *OBE*	Sep 17 / Sep 20
Royal Marines Attaché	Col Neil Sutherland *MBE RM*	Jul 16 / Jul 19
Assistant Military Attaché	Col Nick Lock	Jul 14 / Jul 17
Assistant Air Attaché	Gp Capt Stephen I Richards *RAF*	May 16 / May 19
Counsellor Defence Acquisition and Technology	Mr Simon Gadd	Aug 15 /
Counsellor Defence Policy and Nuclear	Mr Iain King *CBE*	Jan 16 / Jan 19
Head British Defence Liaison Service (North America)	Col Chris Collett	May 14 / May 17

ZAGREB (CROATIA) — (British Embassy, Ivana Lučića 4, 10000 Zagreb, Croatia
Email: british.embassyzagreb@fco.gov.uk   Tel: +385 (1) 6009 100)

Defence section resident in Zagreb with NRA to Hungary (Budapest).

Defence Attaché	Wg Cdr John Kelly	Feb 17 / Jan 21

DEFENCE AND AIR ADVISERS TO
BRITISH HIGH COMMISSIONS

Includes non residential accreditations (NRAs). Listings correct as of March 2018.

ABUJA (NIGERIA) — (British High Commission, Plot 1137, Diplomatic Drive, Central Business District, Abuja, Nigeria
Email: PPAInformation.abuja@fco.gov.uk   Tel: +234 (9) 4623100)

Defence Adviser	Brig Gen Charles Calder	Dec 16 / Dec 19
British Defence Staff West Africa SO1 *& Deputy Defence Adviser*	Cdr Duncan Brodie	Aug 17 / Aug 20

ACCRA (GHANA) — (British High Commission, Julius Nyerere Link, off Gamel Abdul Nasser Avenue, PO Box 296, Accra, Ghana
Email: High.Commission.Accra@fco.gov.uk   Tel: + 233 302 213 250)

Defence section resident in Accra with NRAs to Cote D'Ivoire (Abidjan) and Togo (Lome).

Defence Adviser	Lt Col Simon Westlake *RM*	Apr 16 / Apr 19

BANDAR SERI BEGAWAN (BRUNEI) — (British High Commission, 2.01, 2nd Floor, Block D, Kompleks Bangunan
Yayasan Sultan Haji Hassanal Bolkiah, Jalan Pretty, Bandar Seri Begawan,
PO Box 2197, Brunei
Email: ukinbrunei@fco.gov.uk   Tel: (+673) (2) 222231)

Defence section resident in Bandar Seri Begawan with NRA to Philippines (Manila).

Defence Adviser	Col Mike Page *RM*	Jan 15 / Jan 18

CANBERRA (AUSTRALIA) — (British High Commission, Commonwealth Ave., Yarralumla, Canberra ACT 2600, Australia
Email: australia.enquiries@fco.gov.uk   Tel: +61 (0)2 6270 6666)

Defence section resident in Canberra with NRA to Papua New Guinea (Port Moresby).

Defence and Naval Adviser	Brig Andrew Harrison *DSO MBE*	Jan 17 / Feb 20
Military and Air Adviser	Wg Cdr Jonathan Hough *BA MSc RAF*	Jan 15 / Jan 18

COLOMBO (SRI LANKA) — (British High Commission, 389, Bauddhaloka Mawatha, Colombo 7, Colombo, Sri Lanka
Email: colombo.general@fco.gov.uk   Tel: +94 11 5390639)

Defence section closed in 2009 and responsibility has been with the MOD in London. Point of contact: Level 4 Zone 1 Desk 26, Ministry of Defence, Main Building, Horse Guards Avenue, London SW1A 2HB Email: IPP-SA2@mod.uk.

Defence Adviser	Sqn Ldr David Bond	Nov 15 / Jan 19

DHAKA (BANGLADESH) — (British High Commission, United Nations Road, Baridhara, P O Box 6079, Dhaka - 1212,
Dhaka, Bangladesh
Email: Dhaka.Press@fco.gov.uk   Tel: +880 2 55668700)

Defence Adviser	Lt Col Dom D Spencer	Nov 15 / Jan 19

FREETOWN (SIERRA LEONE) — (British High Commission, 6 Spur Road Freetown, Freetown, Sierra Leone
Email: freetown.general.enquiries@fco.gov.uk   Tel: +232 (0) 78200190)

Defence section resident in Freetown with NRAs to Guinea (Conakry) and Liberia (Monrovia).

Defence Adviser	Cdr Derek Carnell *RN*	Apr 17 / Apr 20

ISLAMABAD (PAKISTAN) — (British High Commission, Diplomatic Enclave, Ramna 5, P O Box 1122, Islamabad, Pakistan
Email: Islamabad-general.enquiries@fco.gov.uk   Tel: +92 51 201 2000)

Defence and Military Adviser	Brig Ben Edwards	Sep 17 / Sep 19
Deputy Defence Adviser	Gp Capt Pete R Daulby	Jan 18 / Jan 20
Military Adviser	Lt Col Ben Ramsay	Jul 17 / Jul 19
Assistant Military Adviser	Maj Yvie Stephens	Mar 18 /

KAMPALA (UGANDA) — (British High Commission, 4 Windsor Loop, P. O. Box 7070, Kampala, Uganda
Email: Kampala.Bhcinfo@fco.gov.uk Tel: +256 (0) 312 312000)
Defence section resident in Kampala with NRAs to Burundi (Bujumbura) and Rwanda (Kigali).

Defence Adviser ....Lt Col Matt Edwards *MBE* .... Mar 18 /

KINGSTON (JAMAICA) — (British High Commission, P O Box 575, 28 Trafalgar Road, Kingston 10, Kingston, Jamaica
Tel: +1 (876) 936 0700)
Defence section resident in Kingston with NRAs - Defence Attaché to Cuba, Dominican Republic and Haiti; Defence Adviser to Bahamas (Nassau), Belize, Guyana, British Dependent Territories (Cayman Islands, Turks & Caicos) and British Overseas Territories (Anguilla, British Virgin Islands & Montserrat).

Defence Adviser ....Lt Col Anton Gash *OBE* ....Apr 17 / Apr 20

KUALA LUMPAR (MALAYSIA) — (British High Commission, Level 27 Menara Binjai, 2 Jalan Binjai, Kuala Lumpur,
50450, Kuala Lumpur, Malaysia
Tel: +6 03 2170 2200)

Defence Adviser ....Col Stephen J Hall ....Mar 15 / Mar 18

NAIROBI (KENYA) — (British High Commission, Upper Hill Road, P.O. Box 30465-00100, Nairobi, Kenya
Email: Nairobi.Enquiries@fco.gov.uk Tel: +254 (0)20 287 3000 / +254 (0)20 2844 000)
Defence section resident in Nairobi with NRAs Defence Adviser to Tanzania (Dar-es-Salaam) and Sychelles (Mahe) .

Defence Adviser ....Brig Mark Christie .... Oct 15 / Oct 18
Military Adviser (British Loan Officer) ....Lt Col Alastair Kern *RM* ....Mar 15 / Mar 18

NEW DELHI (INDIA) — (British High Commission, Shantipath, Chanakyapuri, New Delhi 110021, India
Email: web.newdelhi@fco.gov.uk Tel: +91 (11) 2419 2100)

Defence and Military Adviser ....Brig Mark Goldsack................................... May 15 / Jan 19
Naval and Air Adviser..........................Gp Capt Frazer J.Nicholson..Aug 17 /
Assistant Defence and Military Adviser..........................Lt Col Simon De Labilliere........................... May 15 / May 18

NICOSIA (CYPRUS) — (British High Commission, Alexander Pallis Street, PO Box 21978, Nicosia, 1587, Cyprus
Email: UKinCyprus@fco.gov.uk Tel: +357 22 861100)

Defence Adviser ....Col Martyn Forgrave *QGM OBE*............................Jun 17 / Jun 20

OTTAWA (CANADA) — (British High Commission, 80 Elgin Street, Ottawa Ontario K1P 5K7, Canada
Email: ukincanada@fco.gov.uk Tel: +1 613 237 1530)

Defence and Military Adviser ....Brig Nick Orr ....Feb 18 / Feb 21
Naval and Air Adviser..........................Cdr Neil Marriott *RN* ....Jul 17 / Jul 20
Staff Officer British Defence Liaison Staff...........................Lt Cdr (Retd) Andy Arnold .... Oct 09 /

PRETORIA (SOUTH AFRICA) — (British High Commission, 255 Hill Street, Arcadia, Pretoria, Gauteng, 0002, South Africa
Tel: +27 12 421 7500)
Defence section resident in Pretoria with NRAs to Angola. Naval and Air Adviser is Defence Adviser to Namibia (Windhoek) and Mozambique (Maputo).

Defence and Military Adviser ....Col Alan Litster *RM*...Apr 17 / Apr 20
Naval and Air Adviser...........................Wg Cdr Kevin Rayner .... May 16 / May 19

SINGAPORE (SINGAPORE) — (British High Commission, 100 Tanglin Road, Singapore 247919, Singapore
Email: enquiries.singapore@fco.gov.uk   Tel: (65) 6424 4200)

Defence Adviser ....Cdr Martin Moore *RN*..Jul 17 / Jul 20

British Defence Staff Asia Pacific

British Defence Staff Asia Pacific Chief of Staff...................Col Chris Luckham *OBE*

British Defence Staff Asia Pacific Deputy Chief of Staff......Lt Col Mark Bavin

WELLINGTON (NEW ZEALAND) — (British High Commission, 44 Hill Street, Thorndon, Wellington 6011, New Zealand
Tel: +64 (0) 4 924 2888)

Defence section resident in Wellington with NRAs to Fiji (Suva), Tonga (Nuku'alofa) and Vanuata (Port Vila).
Owing to earthquake damage now lodging with Australian High Commission

Defence Adviser ....Cdr Guy Haywood..Apr 16 / Jul 19

BRITISH LOAN SERVICE TEAMS &
SPECIAL DEFENCE ADVISORY TEAMS

Listing senior commissioned officers only.

BAHRAIN
SO1 Counter-Improvised Explosive Device Capability Development
SO1 C-IED..Lt Col Eamonn Heakin

BRUNEI
British Military Advisor Training Team
RBAF, Bolkiah Camp, Brunei, BFPO 11
Senior British Loan Service Officer.......................................Wg Cdr Jeff Lindsay

CAMEROON
Senior Military Adviser to Cameroon and Chad
British Embassy, Avenue Winston Churchill, Yaounde, Centre Region, 547, Cameroon
Senior Military Adviser...Lt Col Sid Purser *RM*

CZECH REPUBLIC
British Military Advisory Training Team – Central and Eastern Europe
BMATT (CEE), Vojenska Academie, Vita Nejedleho, 682 03 Vyskov 3, Czech Republic
Commander...Col David Cutmur
Chief of Staff..Maj Arthur Frame

JORDAN
British Military Mission
Defence Section, British Embassy, Amman, Jordan, BFPO 747
Commander...Brig Alex Macintosh

KENYA
British Peace Support Team
British Peace Support team, Nairobi, Kenya, BFPO 10
Commander...Col Richard Leakey
Chief of Staff..Maj Michael James
Deputy Chief of Staff...Maj James Rix

KUWAIT
British Military Mission
BMM Kuwait, Box 006, BFPO 635
Commander...Brig Andrew Barr
Director of Studies Kuwait Joint Command &
   Staff College ....Col Timothy Wordsworth

MALAYSIA
Headquarters Integrated Area Defence System
HQ JADS, TUDM Butterworth, 12990 Butterworth, Penang, Malaysia
Director Development...Wg Cdr Colin Would

NIGERIA

British Military Advisory Training Team Nigeria
British High Commission, Abuja, Nigeria, BFPO 5263

Commander..Col Jeremy Bagshaw

Chief of Staff / SO2 Air ....Maj Andrew Hill

OCCUPIED PALESTINIAN TERRITORIES

British Support Team (USSC-R)
British Support Team, FCO Consulate General, Jerusalem, BFPO 5407

Senior British Officer..Brig Johnny Bowron

OMAN

Loan Service Oman
Office of the SBLO, PO Box 113, Post Code 113, Oman

Senior British Loan Service Officer (Oman) ....Maj Gen Richard Stanford

Senior British Loan Service Officer (RN) ....Capt G Pettit *RN*

Senior British Loan Service Officer (Army)..........................Col David Pardy

Senior British Loan Service Officer (RAF) ....Gp Capt Toby Craig

QATAR

Loan Service Qatar
Defence Section, British Embassy, Doha, Qatar, BFPO 5415

SO2 Course Design..Maj Richard Watkins

SAUDI ARABIA

British Military Mission
British Military Mission SANG, PO Box 010, Riyadh, BFPO 5421

Commander British Military Mission to the

   Saudi Arabian National Guard..Brig Stephen Cartwright

Chief of Staff, British Military Mission.................................Lt Col Thomas Wagstaff

   Royal Naval Liaison Team
   Royal Naval Liaison Team, Fing Fahd Naval Academy – Jubail, Riyadh, Saudi Arabia, BFPO 5421

   Officer Commanding Royal Navy Liaison Team ....Lt Cdr Mark Stannard *RN*

   SANGCOM (Saudi Arabia National Guard Communications Project)
   UK MOD SANGCOM Team, Riyadh, Box 10a, Saudi Arabia, BFPO 5421

   Project Director..Brig Peter Drew

   SO1 Training..Lt Col Phillip Deans

   MODSAP (Ministry of Defence Saudi Armed Forces Project)
   UK MOD Team, MODSAP, Riyadh, BFPO 5421

   SO2 Support...Sqn Ldr Derek Heffernan

SIERRA LEONE

International Military Advisory Training Team
IMATT (SL), Leicester Square Camp, Freetown, Sierra Leone, BFPO 622

MOD Adviser..Lt Col Philip Moxham

SOUTH AFRICA

British Peace Support Team

BPST, Pretoria, BFPO 5399

Commander..Col Sacha Tomes

UNITED ARAB EMIRATES (UAE)

British Loan Service Team Abu Dhabi

BLST, c/o Defence Section, British Embassy (Abu Dhabi), BFPO 5413

Senior British Loan Service Officer......................................Capt Jim Lowther *RN*

Signals Adviser ....Lt Col Adam Gray

SO1 EW & INT..Lt Col George Hume

HEADQUARTERS IN THE UNITED KINGDOM OF THE AIR FORCES OF COMMONWEALTH COUNTRIES

(as at 16 February 18)

AUSTRALIA, Defence Staff London

Address: Australia House. Strand, London, WC2B 4LA
(Tel: 020 7379 4334 Fax: 020 7240 5333 Website: www.uk.embassy.gov.au)

Defence Adviser / Head of Australian Defence Staff (HADS) ....Air Cdre Brian Edwards

Air Force Adviser ....Gp Capt Anthony Martin

Assistant Defence Adviser (Strategy) ....Wg Cdr Ruth Elsley

Assistant Defence Adviser ....Lt Col Anthony Evans

CANADA. Canadian Forces, Canadian Defence Liaison Staff

Address: Canada House, Trafalgar Square SW1Y 5BJ
(Tel: 0207 004 6050   Fax: 0207 004 6050   Email: ldn@international.gc.ca   Website: www.unitedkingdom.gc.ca)

Commander-Defence Advisor ....Brig Gen Lowell Thomas

Air Force Advisers ....Col Darcy Molstad

Assistant Air Force Adviser ....Lt Col Tressa Home

INDIA, Military and Air Advisers London

Address: India House, Aldwych, London WC2B 4NA
(Tel: 020 7836 8484   Fax: 020 7836 4331   Email: administration@hcilondon.in   Website: www.hcilondon.in)

Military Adviser...Mr Bhuvana Krishnan Vellore Mohana Krishnan

Air Adviser..Air Cdre Anil Sabharwal

NEW ZEALAND, Defence Staff London

Address: 2nd Floor, New Zealand House, 80 Haymarket Street, London SW1Y 4TQ
(Defence Staff: Tel: 020 7930 8400   Fax: 020 7930 8401   Email: aboutnz@newzealandhc.org.uk)

Defence Adviser & Head New Zealand Defence Staff.................Brig Christopher Parsons

Logistics Adviser ....Lt Cdr Zia Jones

Military Adviser ....Lt Col Katherine Lee

Air Adviser..Wg Cdr Lisa D'Oliveira

PAKISTAN, Defence Staff London

Address: 35-36 Lowndes Square, London SW1X 9JN
(Tel : 020 7664 9276   Fax: 020 7664 9224   Email: phclondon@phclondon.org   Website: www.phclondon.org)

Defence & Naval Adviser ....Cdre Raja Rab Nawaz

Army & Air Adviser..Col Sardar Nadeem Iqbal Khan

Defence Procurement Adviser ....Capt Abdus Sami

SOUTH AFRICA, Defence Staff London

Address: South Africa House, Trafalgar Square, London WC2N 5DP
(Tel: (020) 7451 7299 Fax: (020) 7839 5670)

Defence & Air Advisor...Brig Gen Sithabiso Mahlobo

Deputy Defence & Air Advisor ....Col Daisy Nompumelelo Tshiloane

Defence Office Chief Clerk ....WO1 Nompumelelo Carol Radebe

AIR COMMAND HEADQUARTERS

Address: RAF High Wycombe, Buckinghamshire, HP14 4UE
Tel: (Media Communications Officer) 0149449 Ext 4456
(as at 31 March 2018)

Chief of the Air Staff (COS)..Air Chf Mrshl *Sir* Stephen Hillier
KCB CBE DFC ADC..................................Jul 16

Assistant Chief of the Air Staff (ACAS)..AVM Michael Wigston *CBE (until Aug 18)* ....Jan 17
Air Commdore Air Staff...Air Cdre Richard P Barrow *OBE*............................Jun 16
RAF Corporate Development Officer ....Vacant
Assistant Chief of Staff Media and Communications ....Air Cdre Nigel T Bradshaw 130415

Chief of Staff HQ Air Command..Air Cdre J M Dixon *AFC*.........................161216

Senior Portfolio Director and Transformation Leader ....AVM Malcolm Brecht *CBE*
Head of RAF Transformation ....Air Cdre Alan K Gillespie...................Jun 17

Director of Resources ....Charlie Pate
Head of Secretariat & Civilian Workforce ....Ruth Thompson
Head of Finance...N/D
Head of Resources and Plans ....Catherine Coton

Deputy Commander Operations (DCinC Op)
and Air Member for Operations...AM Stuart D Atha *CB DSO* ....Jun 16
Chief of Staff Operations...AVM Stephen J Shell *OBE* 011216
Assistant Chief of Staff (Operations) ....Air Cdre Lawerence Bennett

No 1 Group (Air Combat Group)
Headquarters, RAF High Wycombe, Walters Ash, High Wycombe, Buckinghamshire, HP14 4UE
Air Officer Commanding 1 Group ....AVM Gerard M D Mayhew *CBE (until Sep 18)*....Apr 16
   Lightning Force Commander ....Air Cdre David G Bradshaw ....Apr 17
   Typhoon Force Commander...Air Cdre Ian W Duguid *OBE (until Mar 18)* ....Mar 15
Air Cdre Mark W J Chappell *(from Mar 18)*
   ISAR Force Commander...Air Cdre Dean R Andrew *OBE (until Oct 18)* 100613
   Air Officer Battle Management & Battle Management
    Force Commander ....Air Cdre Alan K Gillespie *(until Jun 17)*...............040515
Air Cdre Richard D Moir (from Sep 17)
   Joint Force Air Component Commander ....Air Cdre Jeremy J Attridge *OBE ADC*...................Apr 17

No 2 Group (Air Combat Support Group)
Air Officer Commanding 2 Group ....AVM David J E Cooper *CBE*.............................Jun 17
   Air Mobility Force Commander & Air Officer Air Mobility ....Air Cdre Dominic A Stamp *ADC*..........................Jun 17
   Air Officer Force Protection Force Commander &
    Commandant General of the RAF Regiment ....Air Cdre Richard F J Clifford *OBE* ....Apr 16
   Commandant Air Warfare Centre..Air Cdre Alistair J Seymour *(until Nov 18)* ....Dec 15
   Air 2 Group Project GATEWAY Director...................................David J Tozer ....Aug 17

No 38 Group (Transport Group)
Air Officer Commanding (AOC) 38 Group ....AVM Susan C Gray *CB OBE*.............................160616
   Air Officer A6 and A6 Force Commander ....Air Cdre John P Wariner...............................010416
   Air Officer A4 and A4 Force Commander ....Air Cdre Mark Gilligan...............................Jul 16
   Air Officer Medical Operations..Air Cdre Clare S Walton *QHP*.........................Jun 16

Head of RAF Safety Centre...Air Cdre Mark A Jeffery *OBE (RAFVR)*.............190916

**Deputy Commander Capability and Air Member
  for Personnel & Capability (DCOM CAP)**.................AM Sean K P Reynolds *CBE DFC RAF*
                                                    (until Aug 18)..May 16

Chief of Staff Capability (COS - CAP)............................AVM Simon P Rochelle *OBE DFC* ....Apr 17

Assistant Chief of Staff Capability Delivery Combat Air
  and ISTAR ....Air Cdre Lincoln S Taylor *OBE*...........................Dec 14

Assistant Chief of Staff Capability Development ....Air Cdre Julian D Ball *OBE*.................................Mar 17

Assistant Chief of Staff Capability Delivery
  Air Mobility and Air Enablers...Air Cdre David J F Lee *(until Apr 18)* 170715
                                                    Air Cdre Simon Edwards *(from Apr 18)*

Assistant Chief of Staff Capability Delivery C2 ISR..................Air Cdre Ian Gale *MBE*

Chief of Staff Personnel and Air Secretary ....AVM Christina R Elliot *CBE* ....Jul 16

Assistant Chief of Staff Personnel Policy ....Air Cdre Simon A Harper ....Sep 16

Assistant Chief of Staff Career & Talent Management............... Air Cdre Richard J Paul ....Jul 17

Assistant Chief of Staff Manning.................................Air Cdre Adrian Burns

Chaplain-in-Chief...*The Venerable* (AVM) Jonathan P M Chaffey
                                                    QHC BA MA RAF

Director Legal Services (DLS)......................................AVM Alison Mardell..Apr 17

Deputy Director Leghal Services (DDLS)................................Air Cdre Tamara N Jennings *OBE*........................Apr 17

Air Officer Commanding No 22 Group
  and Chief of Staff Training...AVM Warren AW James *CBE*............................... Jul 17

Director Flying Training..Air Cdre David A Bentley *(until Jun 18)* 160115
                                                    Air Cdre James Hunter *(from June 18)*

Director Ground Training and Senior Air Staff
  Officer No 22 Group ....Air Cdre Mark Hunt *OBE* 120617

Commandant Air Cadets ....Air Cdre Dawn A McCafferty *CBE* ....Aug 12

Commandant RAF College Cranwell & DRIT...................Air Cdre Peter J M Squires *OBE* ....Aug 16

Director Defence College of Techincal Training ....Brig Richard Bennett *MVO CEng FIET*...............Apr 16

Head of RAF Medical Services (RAFMS)......................................Air Cdre Stephen C Kilbey *QHP*...........................Dec 14

Assistant Chief of Staff Infrastructure..Air Cdre James E Savage *OBE*.............................180417

JOINT HELICOPTER COMMAND (JHC)

JHC, HQ Land Forces, Marlborough Lines, Monxton Road, Andover SP11 8HJ

Commander JHC ....AVM Richard D Mason *OBE*..Mar 17

Deputy Commander JHC and Head of Operations.............Brig Mike Keating ....Jun 17

Royal Air Force Support Helicopter Force

RAF Benson Station Commander and
  Puma Force Commander...Gp Capt Hamish R C Cormack *MA RAF (until Dec 18)*.......Nov 16
                                                                 Gp Capt A B Wardrope *DFC (from Dec 18)*

RAF Odiham Station Commander and
  UK Chinook Force Commander ....Gp Capt L Turner ....Oct 17

RAF Valley Station Commander ....Gp Capt Nick Tucker-Lowe *DSO MA MCMI RAF* .... Dec 16

RAF Akrotiri Station Commander....................................Gp Capt Mike J Blackburn *MA BSc RAF (until 060718)* 240616

HQ PROVOST MARSHAL (RAF) (HQ PM(RAF))

RAF Honington, Bury St Edmunds, Suffolk IP31 1EE
(Tel: 01359 269561   Website: https://www.raf.mod.uk/our-organisation/force-protection/raf-police/)

Air Officer RAF Police and Commandant
General RAF Regiment..Air Cdre R F J (Frank) Clifford *OBE RAF* ....Apr 16

Office of the Provost Marshal (OPM)
RAF Provost Marshal and Chief of RAF Police...................Gp Capt Steven R Horne *MA RAF*

2 Force Protection Wing:
  1 Tactical Police Squadron (RAF Honington)

3 Force Protection Wing:
  6 RAF Police Squadron (Central England. Based at RAF Marham).

4 Force Protection Wing:
  7 RAF Police Squadron (Southern England) - Security and Guarding for RAF Brize Norton, RAF Benson,
    RAF Northolt, RAF Odiham, RAF St Mawgan and MOD St Athan.

5 Force Protection Wing:
  4 RAF Police Squadron (Northen England and Scotland. Based at RAF Lossiemouth).
  603 (City of Edinburgh) RAuxAF Squadron

7 Force Protection Wing:
  Air Land Integration Cell *(from Summer 2018)*

8 Force Protection Wing:
  5 RAF Police Squadron (North Wales and North Midlands) - Security and guarding for RAF Coningsby, RAF Cranwell,
    RAF Scampton, RAF Valley, RAF Waddington and RAF Wittering.

Other units:
  HQ RAF Police Professional Standards Dept

  No 1 Tactical Provost Squadron

  Forensic Exploitation Flight - digital forensics

  Specialist Investigations Branch (SIB North and SIB South)

  Counter-Intelligence and Security Squadron (CI & Sy)

MILITARY AVIATION AUTHORITY (MAA)

Military Aviation Authority Secretariat
#5102 Level 1, Juniper Building, MOD Abbey Wood, Bristol, BS34 8QW
Email DSA-Enquiries@mod.gov.uk   Website: www.maa.mod.uk

Director General..R Adm Paul A Chivers *OBE*...081215

Director Technical and Chief Technical
    Officer..R Adm R C Thompson *CBE MA BEng(Hons) CEng FRAeS*................031016

Head Oversight & Approvals Group .... Air Cdre Stephen F Lushington *CBE*..Jan 18

Head Regulation and Certification....................Cdre David G Childs..Aug 16

Head Analysis and Plans..................................Ian Hall

ROYAL AIR FORCE COLLEGE

RAF College Cranwell, Sleaford, Lincolnshire, NG34 8HB

Commandant-in-Chief.........................	HM The Queen	
Commandant and Director Recruitment and Initial Training (RAF).................................	Air Cdre Peter J M Squires *OBE ADC MA BEng(Hons)*	.......Aug 16
Group Captain Recruiting & Selection.................................	Gp Capt W Rothery *(until 26 Mar 18)*	.......Jul 16
	Gp Capt W Dole *(from 26 Mar 18)*	
Officer Commanding No 2 Flying Training School (2FTS), RAF Syerston.............................	Gp Capt John Middleton *OBE BA RAFR*	
Officer Commanding No 3 Flying Training School (3FTS), RAF Cranwell..........................	Gp Capt E P Moriarty	.......Dec 17
Officer Commanding No 6 Flying Training School.(6FTS), RAF Cranwell..........................	Gp Capt A Dickens *OBE (until Mar 18)*	.......7 Sep 15
	Gp Capt H Edwards *(from Mar 18)*	

CENTRAL FLYING SCHOOL (CFS)

HQ CFS, RAF College Cranwell, Sleaford, Lincolnshire, NG34 8HB

Commandant CFS..	Gp Capt J F Monahan *OBE DFC MA MSc RAF (until Jun 18)*	.......Mar 16
	Gp Capt A R Franklin *(from Jun 18)*	

Defence Elementary Flying Training School, RAF Barkston Heath, Grantham, Lincolnshire NG32 2DG

Central Flying School (Helicopters) (CFS(H)), RAF Shawbury, Shawbury, Shrewsbury, Shrops SY4 4DZ

Officer Commanding, RAF Shawbury	Gp Capt R S Norris *(until Dec 18)*..	120517
	Gp Capt C A Mullen *(from Dec 18)*	

Defence Helicopter Flying School (DHFS), RAF Shawbury, Shawbury, Shrewsbury, Shrops SY4 4DZ

Commandant	Gp Capt R S Norris	.......Oct 16

No 1 Flying Training School, RAF Linton on Ouse, York, North Yorkshire YO30 2AL

Officer Commanding, RAF Linton on Ouse.....................	Gp Capt C Gleave	.......Dec 16

No 4 Flying Training School, Advanced Fast Jet Training (AFJT), RAF Valley, Holyhead, Isle of Anglesey LL65 3NY

Officer Commanding, RAF Valley.....................................	Gp Capt N A Tucker-Lowe *DSO (until Dec 18)*........................	.......Dec 16
	Gp Capt J D Holmes *OBE (from Dec 18)*	

Multi Engine Advanced Flying Training, RAF College Cranwell, Sleaford, Lincolnshire NG 34 8HB

Central Flying School Association (CFSA)
(Website: www.centralflyingschool.org.uk/)

Patron...	AM *(Retd.) Sir* Graham 'Dusty' Miller *KBE*	2012

Committee

President	AVM Hector G Mackay *CB OBE AFC FRAeS*	2012
Vice-President	Gp Capt J F Monahan *OBE DFC MA MSc RAF*	
Secretary	Wg Cdr Mike Brooks *AFC*	
Tresurer	Sqn Ldr Tim Dean	

DEFENCE COLLEGE OF TECHNICAL TRAINING (DCTT)

MOD Lyneham

Commandant DCTT..Brig Richard Bennett *MVO CEng FIET*................................Apr 16

DEFENCE SCHOOL OF AERONAUTICAL ENGINEERING (DSAE)

HQ DSAE, RAF Cosford, Wolverhampton WV7 3EX

Commandant DSAE and Station
Commander RAF Cosford...Gp Capt Tone Baker *OBE MDA BEng CEng*
MIET RAF...Jun 17

DEFENCE SCHOOL OF COMMUNICATIONS AND INFORMATION SYSTEMS (DSCIS)

HQ DSCIS, Blandford Camp, Blandford Forum DT11 8RE

Commandant DSCIS and Blandford Garrison ....Col Andrew Percival..Mar 16

DEFENCE SCHOOL OF ELECTRONIC AND MECHANICAL ENGINEERING (DSEME)

DSEME Lyneham, MOD Lyneham, Chippenham, Wiltshire SN15 4XX

Commandant DSEME and MOD Lyneham ....Col Ed Heale *OBE* ....Sep 16

DEFENCE SCHOOL OF MARINE ENGINEERING (DSMarE)

HMS Sultan, Military Road, Gosport, Hampshire PO12 3BY

Commandant DSMarE and
Commanding Officer of HMS Sultan ....Capt Peter J Towell *OBE RN* 260716

HEADQUARTERS AIR CADETS

RAF Cranwell, Sleaford, Lincolnshire, NG34 8HB

Honorary Air Commodore-in-Chief Air Training Corps
Her Royal Highness The Duchess of Cambridge

Members of the Air Cadet Council

Chief of the Air Staff...ACM *Sir* Stephen Hillier *KCB CBE DFC ADC*

Vice Patron ....ACM *(Retd.) Sir* Michael Graydon *GCB CBE*

Air Member for Personnel ....AM Sean K P Reynolds *CBE DFC RAF*

Air Officer Commanding No 22 (Training) ....AVM Andrew M Turner *CBE MA MSc BA FRAes FCMI RAF*

Commandant Air Cadets ....Air Cdre Dawn A McCafferty *CBE*

Chief of Staff, HQ Air Cadets ....N/A

Commandant 2 Flying Training School ....Gp Capt John Middleton *OBE BA RAFR*

Regional Chair Central & East Region.............N/A

Regional Chair South West Region ....N/A

Head of the Combined Cadet Force ....Wg Cdr Martin Larwood-Hughes

Corps Chaplain ....Rev James Pitkin

The Air League ....Mr Keith Mans

Air Cadets Regional Headquarters

Central & East Region - ATC Regional Headquarters (C&E), Z Block, RAF Wyton, Huntingdon, Cambs, PE28 2EA
Tel: 01480 52451 (ext. 6774)   Email: ACO-RHQ-CentralEast-E1@mod.uk)   Website: www.centraleast-atc.org.uk

Regional Commandant: Gp Capt Nigel Gorman
Assistant Regional Commandant: Wg Cdr Nathan Wilks

London & South East Region - ATC Region HQ London & SE Air, Bldg 63 RAF Northolt, Ruislip, Middlesex, HA4 6NG
Tel: 0208 8338352 Email: ACO-RHQ-LondonSouthEast-RC@mod.uk Website: www.laseraircadets.org.uk

Regional Commandant: Gp Capt Al Lewis

Wales & West Region - ATC Regional HQ (Wales & West), Boyle Block, RAF Cosford, Wolverhampton WV7 3EX
Tel: 01902 377903   Email: ACO-RHQ-WalesWest-RC@mod.uk

Regional Commandant: Gp Capt Roger Simon

South West Region - ATC Regional Headquarters (South West), Le Marchant Barracks, Franklyn Road, Devizes, Wiltshire,
SN10 2FE   Tel: 01380 739990 (ext. 202)   Email: ACO-RHQ-SouthWest-RC@mod.uk
Website: www.aircadets.info

Regional Commandant: Gp Capt Edward Cole

Scotland & Northern Ireland - ATC Regional Headquarters (Scotland & NI), RAF Leuchars, Nr St Andrews, Fife,
KY16 0JX   Ttel: 01334 857847   Email: ACO-RHQ-AllUsers-SNIRegion@mod.uk

Regional Commandant: Gp Cpt Jim Leggat *OBE*

North Region - ATC Regional Headquarters (North), RAF Linton-on-Ouse, York YO30 2AJ
Tel: 01347 848 261   Email: ACO-RHQ-North-RC@mod.uk   Website: www.aircadetsnorth.org

Regional Commandant: Gp Capt Mark Leeming *OBE*
Assistant Regional Commandant: Ms Mary Jacques

AIR OFFICER SCOTLAND

CUPAR, FIFE

Air Officer Scotland..AVM Ross Paterson *CB OBE ADC DL*..................................171114

AIR OFFICER WALES

(All Media and Correspondence: ROYAL AIR FORCE COMMUNITY RELATIONS OFFICER
THE BARRACKS, BRECON, POWYS LD3 7EA
(Tel: 01874 613 889   Mil: 94351 2889)

Air Officer Wales ....Air Cdre Adrian Williams *OBE*
ADC MA BA FCILT RAF

NATO HEADQUARTERS

Boulevard Leopold III, 1110 Brussels, Belgium
(Nato HQ, Brussels, Belgium BFPO 49)
(as of March 18 unless otherwise stated)

Assistant Secretary General for Operations ....Mr Patrick Turner... Oct 15

INTERNATIONAL MILITARY STAFF

Executive Co-ordinator ....Air Cdre D J Toriati *OBE*...................................... 170916
Director Operations and Plans ....Maj Gen Timothy J Bevis *RM* .... May 16

MILITARY COMMITTEE

NATO Chief of Defence, UK...ACM *Sir* Stuart Peach *KCB CBE ADC BA MPhil DTech*
DLitt FRAeS RAF (until 290618).................... 140716
Prinicipal Staff Officer ....Brig Robaird J Boyd *(from Apr 18)*

UK JOINT DELEGATION TO NATO

UKDel NATO, Boulevard Leopold III, 1110 Brussels, Belgium
(Tel: +32 2 707 7501   Fax: +32 2 707 7596   Email: UKDEL.NATOGeneralEnquiries@fco.gsi.gov.uk)

UK Permanent Representative to the North Atlantic Council ....Ms Sarah MacIntosh CMG................................... Feb 17
UK Military Representative to NATO ....Lt Gen Sir George Norton *KCVO CBE* 200516
Deputy UK Military Representative to NATO ....Brig Richard B Nixon-Eckersall *(until Jun 18)* ... Mar 16

ALLIED COMMAND OPERATIONS (ACO)

Strategic Level Command:

SUPREME HEADQUARTERS ALLIED POWERS EUROPE (SHAPE)

Public Affairs Office, B-7010 SHAPE (Mons), Belgium, BFPO 26
(SHAPE, MONS, Belgium, BFPO 26)
(Tel: +32 (0) 65-44-4154   Fax: +32 (0) 65-44-3100   Email: shapepao@shape.nato.in)

Deputy Supreme Allied Commander Europe (DSACEUR)...................Gen *Sir* James R Everard *KCB CBE*................... Mar 17
Chief of Staff, Supreme Allied Command...AM *Sir* Graham Stacey *CB MBE (until Dec 18)* ...Jan 18
V Adm Paul Bennett *CB OBE (from Dec 18)*
United Kingdom National Military Representative, Supreme HQ.........Air Cdre Anthony J Beasant 240417
Director Comprehensive Crisis and Operations Management Centre ....Brig Jasper J De Quincey....................................... Jul 17

Operational Level Commands:

JOINT FORCE COMMAND HEADQUARTERS (JFC) BRUSSNUM

HQ Allied JFC BRUNSSUM, Public Affairs Office, Box 270, 6440 AG Brunssum, The Netherlands
(NATO JFC, Holland, BFPO 28)   (Email: pao@jfcbs.nato.int)

Deputy Commander (DCOM JFCBS)..AM Graham E Stacey *CB MBE MA*
BSc CCMII (until Jun 17)............................ 17 Oct 15
Deputy Chief of Staff Plans ....Maj Gen L Karl Ford .... Sep 17
Director of Management and Senior British Officer.............................Air Cdre Andrew D Huggett.......................... 20 Nov 15

Resolute Support Headquarters (Afghanistan)
(Tel: +93 (0)70-013-2114 / +93 (0)70-013-2928   Website: www.rs.nato.int)

Resolute Support Mission Deputy Commander ....Lt Gen Richard Cripwell *CB CBE*....................... Oct 17
NATO Air Command Deputy Commander (Afghanistan) ....Air Cdre James H Hunter *(until Apr 18)*.............. Oct 17
Air Cdre J Burr *CBE DFC (from Apr 18)*

JOINT FORCE COMMAND HEADQUARTERS (JFC NAPLES)
Allied Joint Force Command Naples, Via Madonna del Pantano, 80014 Lago Patria,
Giugliana in Campania, Naples, Italy
(NATO JFC, NAPLES, Italy, BFPO 8)
(Tel: 081-721-2752 / 081-721-3838   Email: http:JFCNPPAOGROUP@jfcnp.nato.int)

Deputy Chief of Staff Plans .... Maj Gen Ian Cave *(until May 18)*
Maj Gen Gary C Deakin *(from May 18)*

Tactical Level Commands

ALLIED AIR COMMAND (HQ AIRCOM)

HQ AIRCOM, Public Affairs Office - Büro für Öffentlichkeitsarbeit, Building/Gebäude 313, Flugplatz Ramstein, D-66877
Ramstein-Miesenbach, Germany (BFPO 109)
(Email: airn.pao@airn.nato.int   Website: www.airn.nato.int)

Deputy Commander Allied Air Command (DCOM AIRCOM) .... AM Stuart C Evans *CBE* .... Aug 16

ALLIED LAND COMMAND (HQ LANDCOM)

NATO Land Command, General Vecihi Akin Garrison 35148 Izmir / TURKEY
(Email: lc.registry@lc.nato.int   Website: www.lc.nato.int)

ALLIED MARITIME COMMAND (HQ MARCOM)

Atlantic Building, Northwood Headquarters, Sandy Lane, Northwood, Middlesex, HA6 3HP
(Tel: 01923 956 763 (Public Affairs Office)   Email: publicaffairs@mc.nato.int   Website: www.mc.nato.int)

Commander .... V Adm Clive C Johnstone *CB CBE* .... Oct 15

Command Senior Enlisted Leader .... WO Ian Anderson

Tactical Air C2 Elements:

NATO CIS GROUP (NCISG)
(Based in Mons. Belgium)

NAVAL STRIKING AND SUPPORT FORCES NATO (STRIKFORNATO)
Reduto Gomes Freire, Estrada Da Medrosa, 2780 - 070 Oeiras, Portugal
(Tel: +351 21 440 4116 (Public Affairs Office)   E-mail: pao@sfn.nato.int   Website: hwww.sfn.nato.int)

Deputy Commander .... R Adm Guy A Robinson .... Nov 17

NATO AIRBORNE EARLY WARNING AND CONTROL FORCE COMMAND (NAEW&CF)

NATO AEW and CF, P.O. Box 40800, Lilienthalallee 100, 52511 Geilenkirchen, Germany
(Tel: +49 (0) 2451 63 2485 (Public Affairs Office)   Fax: +49 (0) 2451 7936 (Public Affairs Office)
Email: ofc-hqfhp@naew.nato.int   Website: www.e3a.nato.int)

E-3D Component, RAF Waddington, Lincoln LN5 9NB

Deputy Commander and Chief of Staff (HQ) .... Air Cdre Andrew T Martin *OBE* 210717

Commander E-3D Component .... Wg Cdr Jez Batt

RAPIDLY DEPLOYABLE CORPS HEADQUATERS
Headquarters Allied Command Europe Rapid Reaction Corps (ARRC)

HQ ARRC, Imjin Barracks, Innsworth, Gloucester GL3 1HW
(Tel: +44(0)1452 718007 Fax: +44(0)1452 718875
Email: pao.admin@arrc.nato.int   Website: www.arrc.nato.int)

Commander (COMARRC)	Lt Gen Timothy B Radford *CB DSO OBE*	250716
Chief of Staff	Maj Gen J F Bramble	Dec 16
Deputy Chief of Staff (Support)	Brig Jonathan R. H. Timmis	Jan 18
Assistant Chief of Staff (Communications)	Brig Paul R Griffiths	Aug 16
Chief Engineer	Brig Kevin M Copsey	Sep 16
Chief, Joint Fires and Influence	Brig Paul P Tennant	Oct 15
Command Sergeant Major	Maj Allan Ridler	230117

Headquarters Rapid Reaction Corps-France (HQ RRC-FR)

Deputy Chief of Staff, Support ....Brig Christopher Rose

Headquarters Rapid Deployable Corps Italy (NRDC-ITA)

Via per Busto Arsizio, 20, 21058 Solbiate Olona (VA), Italy
(Tel: +39 0331 34 5111 (Switchboard)   Email: nrdcitapaoweb@gmail.com   Website: www.nrdc-ita.nato.int)

Deputy Commander ....Maj Gen Sir Edward A Smyth-Osbourne
KCVO CBE .... Jul 16

ALLIED COMMAND TRANSFORMATION (ACT)

HQ SUPREME ALLIED COMMAND TRANSFORMATION (HQ SACT)

Public Affairs Office, 7857 Blandy Road, Suite 100, Norfolk, VA23551-2490, USA, BFPO493
(Tel: +1 (757) 747-3600   Fax: +1 (757) 747-3234   E-mail: pao@act.nato.int
Website: www.act.nato.int   Email: pao@act.nato.int)

Chief of Staff to Supreme Allied Commander Transformation ....AM *Sir* Graham E Stacey *KBE CB* 111215

Joint Warfare Centre (JWC)
Joint Warfare Centre, PO Box 8080, Eikesetveien, 4068 Stavanger, Norway
(Tel: + (47) 52 87 9130/9131/9132   Email: pao@act.nato.int)

Joint Force Training Centre (JFTC)
Joint Force Training Centre, Central Registry , ul. Szubinska 2, 85-915 Bydgoszcz, Poland
(Tel: +48 261 41 9777   Fax: +48 261 41 1579   Email: JFTC@jftc.nato.int   Website: www.jftc.nato.int)

Joint Analysis and Lessons Learned Centre
Avenida Tenente Martins, Monsanto, 1500-589 Lisboa, Portugal
(Tel: + 351 21 771 7007/8/ 9   Email: jallc@jallc.nato.int   Website: www.jallc.nato.int)

ORGANISATIONS AND AGENCIES

COMBINED JOINT OPERATIONS FROM THE SEA CENTRE OF EXCELLENCE (CJOS COE)
1562 Mitscher Ave., Suite 250, Norfolk, VA 23551-2487
(Website: www.cjoscoe.org)

Deputy Director, Combined Joint Operations.....................................Cdre Thomas Guy ....Sep 17

COMBINED AIR AND SPACE OPERATIONS CENTRE (CAOC)
Al Udeid, Qatar

Director ....Air Cdre Harvey Smyth *OBE DFC* ....Jul 17

EUROPEAN UNION MILITARY COMMITTEE

European External Action Service , 9A Rond Point Schuman, 1046 Brussels, Belgium
(Tel: +32 2 584 11 11   Website: /eeas.europa.eu)

UK Military Representative to NATO ....Lt Gen *Sir* George Norton *KCVO CBE* ....May 16

EUROPEAN DEFENCE AGENCY

Rue des Drapiers, 17-23, B-1050 Ixelles, Belgium
(Tel: +32 25042800   Fax: +32 25042815   Email: info@eda.europa.eu   Website: www.eda.europa.eu)

Director Capability, Armament & Technology ....Air Cdre Pete Round *(until Mar 17)* ....Jul 12

EUROPEAN EXTERNAL ACTION SERVICE (EEAS)

EEAS Building, 9A Rond Point Schuman, 1046 Brussels, Belgium
(Tel: +32 2 584 11 11   Website: https://eeas.europa.eu)

Senior Military Adviser, Crisis Management and
Planning Directorate ....Air Cdre John D Maas 031014

EUROPEAN UNION

Deputy UK Military Representative ....Brig Matthew Pierson *RM*

UNITED NATIONS

Department of Peacekeeping Operations
(https://peacekeeping.un.org)

Deputy Military Adviser ....Maj Gen Adrian Foster

OTHER INTERNATIONAL APPOINTMENTS

Deputy Commanding General, Task Force Phantom...Maj Gen Douglas Chalmers

Director, Afghan Ministry of the Interior Ministerial Advisor Group ....Maj Gen Charles Herbert

Deputy Commander, Strategy & Support for Operation Inherent Resolve ....Maj Gen Felix Gedney

Commander, U.K. Maritime Component, Bahrain..Cdre Steve Dainton *CBE*

Head of Nuclear Operations, U.S. Strategic Command...Cdre Paul Burke *OBE*

Commander, Standing NATO Maritime Group Two ....Cdre James Morley

Deputy Director, International Logistics & Security Co-operation, U.S. Pacific Command ....Brig Rory Copinger-Symes *RM*

Chief Mentor, Afghan National Army Officer Academy..Brig Ian Rigden

Deputy Commander, NATO Special Operations HQ ....Brig Angus Fair

Deputy Commanding General, 3rd (French) Division ....Brig Nicholas Nottingham *OBE*

Senior British Officer, U.S. Security Co-ordinator, Palestine...Brig Mark Thornhill

Deputy Director, Strategy, Plans and Policy, U.S. Central Command...................................Brig James Learmont *CBE*

Chief of Staff, U.N. Mission to South Sudan..Brig Robaird Boyd

Chief Mentor, Afghan National Army Officer Academy ....Brig David Colthup

Commander, Kabul Security Force and British Troops, Afghanistan....................................Brig Nicholas Pond

COMMONWEALTH WAR GRAVES COMMISSION (CWGC)

2 Marlow Road, Maidenhead, Berkshire SL6 7DX
(Tel: +44 (0)1628 634221 (English Enquiries)   Tel: +32 (0) 57224750 (French, Dutch and German Enquiries)
Email: enquiries@cwgc.org   Website: www.cwgc.org)

(as of 31 March 2018)

Commissioners

President...*HRH The Duke of* Kent *KG GCMG*
GCVO ADC(P)...270270

Chairman...*The Rt Hon* Gavin Williamson *CBE MP*
(The Secretary of State for Defence (UK))

Vice Chairman ....V Adm *Sir* Tim Laurence *KCVO CB ADC(P)* 010716

Representatives of Member Governments

New Zealand ....*HE The Rt Hon Sir* Jerry Mateparae *GNZM*
QSO KST...Mar 17

Australia...*HE The Hon* Alexander Downer *AC (until May 18)* .2014

South Africa ....*HE* Ms NomatembaTambo .... Mar 18

Canada..*HE* MME Janice Charette.....................................Sep 16

Republic of India...*HE* Mr Yashvardhan Kumar Sinha ....Feb 17

Members ....Prof *Sir* Hew Strachan *PhD FRSE*......................Mar 06
The Rt Hon Keith Simpson *MP* 2008
The Rt Hon Kevan Jones *MP*...................................2010
Mr Edward Chaplin *CMG OBE*..............................2011
The Hon Mrs Ros Kelly *AO*....................................2012
Mr Robert Fox *MBE*...2012
Lt Gen *Sir* William Rollo *KCB CBE* 2013
AM Daivd Walker *CB CBE AFC*............................2016

Executive Directors

Director General (Secretary of the Commission) ....Victoria Wallace.......................................201014

Director of Human Resources..Jamie Redmond

Director of Operations ....Barry Murphy ....May 15

Director of Resources ....Judith O'Connell....................................May 15

Director of Information and Communications...Liz Woodfield.......................................May 17

General Counsel..Stuart Davis...Sep 17

Director of International and Community Engagement.........................Julian Evans .... Nov 17

United Kingdom & Northern Area
CWGC, 2 Marlow Road, Maidenhead, Berkshire SL6 7DX
(Tel: +44 (0) 1628 634221   Fax: +44 (0) 1628 771208   E-mail: enquiries@cwgc.org)
Director ....Chris Lee

Western Europe Area
Elverdingestraat 82 , B-8900 Ieper , Belgium
(Tel: +32 (0) 57 22 36 36   Fax: +32 (0) 57 21 80 14   E-mail: contact.wea@cwgc.org)

Director Operations..Richard Nichol

Director External Relations...Liz Sweet

France

5 -7 Rue Angèle Richard CS1019, 62217 Beaurains, France

(Tel: +33 (0) 3 21 21 77 00   Fax: +33 (0) 3 21 21 77 10   E-mail: contact.wea@cwgc.org)

Mediterranean Area

CWGC, PO Box 40970, TT 6308, Cyprus

(Tel: +357 24819460   Fax: +357 24661969   E-mail: maoffice@cwgc.org)

Director ....Ian Hussein

Africa & Asia Pacific Area

CWGC, 2 Marlow Road, Maidenhead, Berkshire SL6 7DX

(Tel: +44 (0) 1628 634221   Fax: +44 (0) 1628 771643   E-mail: aapaoffice@cwgc.org)

Director ....Richard Hills

Australia

Office of Australian War Graves Department of Veterans' Affairs GPO Box 9998

Canberra ACT 2601, Australia

(Tel: +61 (0) 2 6289 6477   Fax: +61 (0) 2 6289 4861   E-mail: wargraves@dva.gov.au)

Canada

Canadian Agency, CWGC, 66 Slater Street, Suite 1412

Ottawa, Ontario K1A 0P4 , Canada

(Tel: +1 613 992 3224   Fax: +1 613 995 0431

E-mail: enquiries@cwgc.org   Web Site: www.cwgc-canadianagency.ca)

Secretary-General...Brig Gen (Retd) David Kettle

New Zealand

Heritage Operations, Ministry for Culture and Heritage PO Box 5364,

Wellington, New Zealand

(Tel: +64 (0) 4 499 4229   Fax: +64 (0) 4 499 4490   E-mail: info@mch.govt.nz)

South Africa

South African Agency

c/o Africa, Asia and Pacific Area CWGC Head Office

2 Marlow Road , Maidenhead, Berkshire, SL6 7DX

Director ....Juan Maree

RESERVE FORCES & CADETS ASSOCIATIONS (RFCAs)

THE COUNCIL OF RESERVE FORCES & CADETS ASSOCIATIONS (CRFCA)

Holderness House, 51-61 Clifton Street, London EC2A 4EY
Tel: 020 7426 8350 Email: co-info@rfca.mod.uk
Website: www.gov.uk/government/organisations/reserve-forces-and-cadets-associations

RFCA Governance
(As of annual report 2016/2017)

President.................................*The Rt Hon The Lord* de Mauley *TD*
Chairman...............................Lt Gen (Retd) Robin V Brims *CB CBE DSO DL*
Board Chairman.....................Capt I M Robinson *OBE RD RNR*
Vice-Chairmen.......................Army...... Maj Gen (Retd) S F N Lalor *CB TD*
Marines . Brig T H Lang *QVRM RD* DL*
Air .... Air Cdre I R W Stewart *CBE BSc FRAeS*
Navy......Capt N R V Dorman *RD ADC RNR*

Council Secretariat

Chief Executive.......................Maj Gen (Retd) J H Gordon *CB CBE*...010916
Chief of Staff..........................Brig Mark P Banham *MBE*
Director Cadets & Youth........Cdr G R Bushell *RN*
Director Volunteer Estates .....Mr S Blissitt *MSc*
Director Engagement ....Mr S Crookbain
Secretary Pension Scheme .....Mr I Scarfe

The 13 Reserve Forces' and Cadets' Associations (RFCAs) are Crown Agencies, established by Act of Parliament under the Reserve Forces Act 1996. Each one is a separate, independent and autonomous Tri-Service corporate body with a function to support the Reserve Forces and Cadets.

Each RFCA is represented on the CRFCA by its chairman.

Board Members..................... Maj Gen G S Smith *CB QVRM TD* ....(Chairman East Anglia RFCA)
Col R M L Colville *TD DL*...................................(Chairman East Midlands RFCA)
Col M A J M Overton *TD*....................................(Chairman Greater London RFCA)
Capt N R V Dorman *RD ADC RNR* ....(Chairman Highland RFCA)
Col Allan C C Lapsley *QVRM TD DL*...................(Chairman Lowland RFCA)
Col Nick D O Williams *TD JP DL* ....(Chairman North West &
Isle of Man RFCA)
Col H K McAllister *OBE TD VR*...........................(Chairman Northern Ireland RFCA)
Lt Gen Robin V Brims *CB CBE DSO DL* ....(Chairman North of England RFCA)
Col W M J Partridge *TD DL* ....(Chairman South East RFCA)
Capt Brian J Thorne *RD DL RNR*.......................(Chairman Wales RFCA)
Gp Capt M R Trace *OBE DL MA FRaES RAF*.....................(Chairman Wessex RFCA)
Col *The Hon.* Philip S Seccombe *TD FRICS*.......................(Chairman West Midland RFCA)
Brig D A Hargreaves...(Chairman Yorkshire &
The Humber RFCA)

EAST ANGLIA

President

Helen Nellis *BA (Hons) MA Barrister*
(HM Lord-Lieutenant of Bedford)

Chairman

Maj Gen G S Smith *CB QVRM TD*

Chief Executive

Col (Retd) Ray K Wilkinson *QVRM TD VR*

Deputy Chief Executive

Lt Col J A Allan *QVRM TD VR*

Association address

Springfield Tyrells, 250 Springfield Road,
Chelmsford, Essex CM2 6BU
Tel: 01245 244800/801
DFTS: 94660 4800/4801
Fax: 01245 492398
DFTS Fax: 94660 4823
Email: ea-info@rfca.mod.uk
Website: www.earfca.org.uk

EAST MIDLANDS

President

Lady Jennifer Gretton *JP*
(HM Lord-Lieutenant of Leicestershire)

Chairman

Col R M L (Murray) Colville *TD DL*

Chief Executive

Gp Capt (Retd) Nick D Sharpe

Deputy Chief Executive

Lt Col P S P (Simon) Worsley *RA*

Association address

Army Reserve Centre, Triumph Road,
Lenton, Nottingham NG7 2GG
Tel: 0115 924 8610
DFTS: 94451 5610
Fax: 0115 924 8629
Email: em-enquiries@rfca.mod.uk
Website: www.eastmidlandsrfca.co.uk

GREATER LONDON

President

Mr Kenneth Olisa *OBE FRSA FBCS*
(HM Lord-Lieutenant of Greater London)

Chairman

Col Marc A J M Overton *TD VR*

Chairman City RFCA

Capt Paul Hill *RD RNR*

Chief Executive

Col (Retd) Hugh M Purcell *OBE DL*

Head of Youth & Cadets and Chief of Staff

Lt Cdr Anthony Pringle *MRAeS MCMI MCGI*

Head of Engagement

Mr Niall Ahern *BSc MA (RAuxAF)*

Head of Estates & Commerical Lettings

Mr Nick Summers *BSc FRICS FB Eng*

Association address
Fulham House, 87 Fulham High
Street, London SW6 3JS
Tel: 020 7384 4640   DFTS: 94624 4640
Fax: 020 7384 4660   DFTS Fax: 94624 4660
Email: gl-offman@rfca.mod.uk
Website: www.glrfca.org

HIGHLANDS

President

R Adm A Michael Gregory *OBE*
(HM Lord-Lieutenant of Dunbartonshire)

Chairman

Capt N R V Dorman *RD ADC RNR*

Vice-Chairmen

R Adm Chris Hockley *CBE*, Col J A B Kinloch *TD*
Wg Cdr D Caddick *MBE RAuxAF*

Chief Executive

Brig (Retd) M P Dodson *MBE*

Deputy Chief Executive

Lt Col A Macnaughton

Association address:
Seathwood, 365 Perth Road, Dundee DD2 1LX
Tel: 01382 668283
Fax: 01382 566442
Email: hi-offadmin@rfca.mod.uk
Website: www.hrfca.co.uk

LOWLANDS

President

Mr Guy W N H Clark *FCSI JP*
(HM Lord-Lieutenant of Renfrewshire)

Chairman

Col Allan C C Lapsley *QVRM TD DL*

Chief Executive

Col (Retd) Robbie D Gibson *OBE*

Deputy Chief Executive

Col (Retd) Tom C Mathew

Association address

Lowland House,
60 Avenuepark Street, Glasgow G20 8LW
Tel: 0141 945 4951
DFTS: 94535 2014
Fax: 0141 945 4869
Email: lo-offman@rfca.mod.uk
Website: www.lowlandrfca.org.uk

NORTHERN IRELAND

President

Col Denis Desmond *CBE*
(HM Lord-Lieutenant of Londonderry)

Chairman

Col H K McAllister *OBE TD VR*

Chief Executive

Col John W Rollins *MBE*

Deputy Chief Executive

Lt Col Antony D Sykes *MBE QGM BEM*

Association contact

25 Windsor Park,
Belfast BT9 6FR

Tel: 02890 665024
Fax: 02890 662809
Email: ni-offman@rfca.mod.uk
Website: www.reservesandcadetsni.org.uk

NORTH WEST OF ENGLAND AND ISLE OF MAN

President

Mr Warren Smith *KStJ JP DLitt LLD*
(HM Lord-Lieutenant of Greater Manchester)

Chairman

Col Nick D O Williams *TD JP DL*

Chief Executive

Col Mark C H Underhill *OBE*

Deputy Chief Executive

Col Alex F Barnes

Association address

Alexandra Court,
28 Alexandra Drive, Liverpool L17 8YE
Tel: 0151 727 4552
DFTS: 94552 8164
Fax: 0151 727 8133
DFTS Fax: 94552 8133
Email: nw-info@rfca.mod.uk
Website: www.nwrfca.org.uk

NORTH OF ENGLAND

President

Mrs S Snowdon
(HM Lord-Lieutenant of County Durham)

Chairman

Lt Gen Robin V Brims *CB CBE DSO DL*

Chief Executive

Brig Paul J A Baker *OBE*

Deputy Chief Executive

Lt Col J I Clyde

Association address

53 Old Elvet,
Durham DH1 3JJ
Tel: 0191 383 6250
Fax: 0191 384 0918
Email: ne-info@rfca.mod.uk
Website: www.rfca-ne.org.uk

SOUTH EAST

President
Mr N J B Atkinson
(HM Lord-Lieutenant of Hampshire)

Chairman
Col W M J Partridge *TD DL*

Chief Executive
Col Patrick T Crowley

Head of Engagement/ COS
Gp Capt K Lane

Head of Cadets & Youth
Lt Col P G B Ellis *QGM**

Association address
Seely House, Shoe Lane,
Aldershot, Hampshire GU11 2HJ
Tel: 01252 357604
Fax: 01252 357620
Email: se-offman@rfca.mod.uk
Website: www.serfca.org

WALES

President
Dame Shan Legge-Bourke *DCVO*
(HM Lord-Lieutenant for Powys)

Chairman
Capt Brian J Thorne *RD DL RNR*

Chief Executive
Col Nick R Beard *DL*

Deputy Chief Executive
Lt Col Stephen M M Hughes *MSc BSc(Econ)*

Association address
Centre Block, Maindy Barracks,
Cardiff CF14 3YE
Tel: 02920 220251
DFTS: 94355 8205
Fax: 02920 224828
DFTS Fax: 94355 8313
Email: wa-offyandc@rfca.mod.uk
Website: www.wales-rfca.org

WESSEX

President
Mr Angus Campbell
(HM Lord-Lieutenant of Dorset)

Chairman
Gp Capt M R Trace *OBE DL MA FRaES RAF*

Chief Executive
Brig Steve P Hodder *(late RE)*

Deputy Chief Executive
Lt Col Peter G Adams *BSc (Hons) MSc*

Association address
Mount House, Mount Street,
Taunton, Somerset TA1 3QE
Tel: 01823 254571
Fax: 01823 259935
Email: wx-offman@rfca.mod.uk
Website: www.wessex-rfca.org.uk

WEST MIDLANDS

President
Mr Ian J Dudson *CBE CStJ*
(HM Lord-Lieutenant of Staffordshire)

Chairman
Col *The Hon.* Philip S Seccombe *TD FRICS*

Vice Chairman (Air)
AVM Mike Smart *DL*

Chief Executive
Col Tim F L Weeks *OBE*

Deputy Chief Executive
Maj M Young

Association address
Tennal Grange, Tennal Road,
Harborne, Birmingham B32 2HX
Tel: 0121 427 5221
Fax: 0121 427 8380
Email: wm-info@rfca.mod.uk
Website: www.wmrfca.org

YORKSHIRE AND THE HUMBER

President

Andrew J Coombe
(HM Lord-Lieutenant of South Yorkshire)

Chairman

Brig D A Hargreaves

Chief Executive

Col (Retd) Jason K Wright

Deputy Chief Executive

Lt Col (Retd) J D Bleasdale

Association address

20 St George's Place,
York YO24 1DS
Tel: 01904 623081
DFTS: 94777 2568
Fax: 01904 622245
Email: yh-info@rfca.mod.uk
Website: www.rfca-yorkshire.org.uk

NAVY, ARMY AND AIR FORCE INSTITUTES (NAAFI)

NAAFI Building 1/150, Room 103, Murrays Lane (PP19B),
HM Naval Base Portsmouth, Portsmouth Hampshire, PO1 3NH

Website: www.naafi.co.uk

PATRON – HM THE QUEEN

Board of Management

Managing Director .... Steve Marshall
NAAFI Chairman .... *Sir* Ian Prosser
Non-Executive Directors .... Reg Curtis
Alan Smith *BA FRAeS*
Gen *Sir* Redmond Watt *KCB KCVO CBE*

NAAFI Council

NAAFI Chairman .... Sir Ian Prosser
Chief of Defence Staff .... ACM *Sir* Stuart Peach *GBE KCB ADC DL*
Commander Home Command .... Lt Gen James Bashall *CBE*
Second Sea Lord .... V Adm Anthony D Radakin
Air Member for Personnel & Capabilities .... AM Sean K P Reynolds *CBE DFC*
Chief of Joint Operations .... Lt Gen *Sir* John Lorimer *KCB DSO MBE*
Defence Infrastructure Organisation Operations

GRADATION LIST
of Officers Serving on the Active List

Marshals of the Royal Air Force

HRH The Prince Philip, Duke of Edinburgh, KG KT OM GBE ONZ AC QSO GCL CC CMM PC ADC(P) psc(n)......15 Jan 53

HRH The Prince of Wales, KG KT GCB OM AK QSO PC ADC(P)..16 Jun 12

FORMER CHIEFS OF THE AIR STAFF

Marshals of the Royal Air Force

Williamson, Sir Keith GCB AFC reds psc cfs* ....15 Oct 85

Craig of Radley, The Lord GCB OBE MA DSc FRAeS reds psc cfs...14 Nov 88

Harding, Sir Peter Robin GCB...6 Nov 92

Stirrup, The Lord Graham E, KG GCB AFC FRAeS FCMI ....14 Jun 14

Air Chief Marshals

Torpy, Sir Glenn L, GCB CBE DSO ....13 Apr 06

Dalton, Sir Stephen GG, GCB CB ADC LLD BSc FRAeS CCMI hcsc psc qwi..1 Apr 09

Pulford, Sir Andrew D, GCB KCB CBE ADC RAF hcsc psc...22 Jul 13

AIR RANK LIST

Listing senior RAF officers 1-star rank and above, as of 04 Jan 18
File source: `www.raf.mod.uk - 2018_AirForce List_ 1 Star and above' [.xlsx]

Chief of Defence Staff

Peach, Sir Stuart W, GBE KCB ADC DL hcsc psc qwi (t)..18 Jul 16

Air Chief Marshals

Hillier, Sir Stephen J, KCB CBE DFC MA RAF rcds hcsc psc cfs...11 Jul 16

Cousins, Sir David , KCB AFC ....01 Aug 97

Dalton, Sir Stephen GG, GCB ADC LLD BSc FRAeS CCMI ....01 Apr 09

Air Marshals

MacFadyen, Sir Ian D, KCVO CB OBE ....26 Aug 94

Walker, Sir David A, CB CBE AFC ....29 Aug 03

Sturley, Philip O, CB MBE FRAeS..31 Oct 03

Anderson, Sir Timothy M, KCB,DSO..15 Mar 07

Harper, Sir Christopher N, KBE MA CMgr CCMI ....31 Mar 09

Stacey, Graham E, CB MBE MA QCVS BSc rcds hcsc(j) psc(m) g(a)...10 Jan 13

North, Sir Barry M, KCB OBE MA FRAeS RAF..03 May 13

Osborn, Philip C, CBE hcsc psc qwi (t)..25 Jan 15

Young, Julian A, CB OBE CEng FIET rcds psc ....26 Apr 16

Reynolds, Sean KP, CBE DFC hcsc(j) psc(j) cfs..09 May 16

Atha, Stuart D, CB DSO hcsc psc(j) cfs ....27 May 16

Evans, Stuart C, CBE MSc FIET hcsc(j) psc cfs qwi (t) ....05 Aug 16

Air Vice-Marshals

Mackay, Hector G, CB OBE AFC BSc FRAeS.. 01 Jan 01

Dougherty, Simon RC, QHP MSc FFOM DAvMed DObstRCOG FCMI FRAeS RAF.......................17 Sep 04

Bairsto, Nigel A, CB MBE MDA MSc BSc CEng. FIMechE FRAeS FCMI RAF .... 01 Dec 05

Beaverbrook, Lord, Maxwell W ....05 Jul 09

Howard, Graham J, CB MA FCILT RAF .... 27 May 11

Morrison, Ian C, CBE ....12 Sep 11

Farnell, Graham P, CB OBE psc(j)..30 Jul 12

Brecht, Malcolm AB, CBE MA BA FRAeS hcsc(j) psc(j)...02 Nov 12

Stringer, Edward J, CBE MA BEng hcsc psc qwi ....05 Apr 13

West, Margaret E, CBE qss..01 Aug 13

Stubbs, David J, CB OBE MCGI FRAeS RAF psc(j)...29 Nov 13

Gray, Susan C, CB OBE MSc FIET psc(j) ....29 Jan 14

Air Vice-Marshals - contd.

Turner, Andrew M, CBE MA MSc BA FRAes FCMI RAF hcsc(j) psc qab qhti ....18 Jul 14

Chaffey, Jonathan PM, QHC MA BA...25 Jul 14

Waterfall, Gary M, CBE hcsc(j) qwi qs qss1 ....12 Sep 14

Broadbridge, The Hon Richard JM, QHS MBA MB BS MRCGP FRAeS FCMI ....19 Dec 14

Wigston, Michael, CBE MA MA hcsc(j) psc(j) qwi (t)..20 Jan 15

Knighton, Richard J, CB psc(j)..23 Jan 15

Parker, Gavin DA, OBE MA BSc (Hons) psc(j)..23 Jun 15

Corbett, Anthony S, MBE psc(j)..26 Oct 15

Mayhew, Gerard MD, CBE ....28 Apr 16

Hedley, Bruce H, MBE ADC MA psc(j) qwi.. 09 May 16

Tunnicliffe, Garry, psc(j).. 27 Jun 16

Bethell, Keith HR, CBE BSc MA MSc CEng FRAeS RAF psc(j)..................................... 04 Jul 16

Elliot, Christina R, CBE psc(j) ....21 Jul 16

Russell, Graham M, MA BSc C Eng FRAeS RAF psc(j)..01 Aug 16

Shell, Stephen J, OBE hcsc(j) psc(j), ... 07 Dec 16

Luck, Christopher J, MBE MA MPhil FRSA FCMI FRAeS..10 Feb 17

Quigley, Michael, MA MSc CEng MIET FIExpE psc(j)..01 Apr 17

Rochelle, Simon P, OBE DFC MA hcsc(j) psc(j) qwi (t) ....21 Apr 17

Mardell, Alison, LLM MA RAF ....29 Apr 17

James, Warren AW, CBE MA CMgr FCMI .... 08 Jun 17

Cooper, David JE, CBE .... 14 Jun 17

Hart, Michael P ....30 Oct 17

Sampson, Martin E, CBE DSO MA psc(j) qwi .... 01 Jan 18

Air Commodores

Trenchard, Hugh ....21 Apr 06

Paterson, Ross, CB OBE ADC DL BSc..01 Jul 06

Williams, Robert A, OBE psc ....01 Jul 06

Cooper, Barbara, CBE...01 Jan 08

Mozumder, Aroop K, CB QHP MSc MB BS MRCSEng MRCGP FRCP DRCOG DTM&H DAvMed DMCC Dip IoD......01 Jun 08

Opie, Gerard A, MDA MA BSc FCIPD RAF psc(j) ....01 Jul 08

Atkinson, Richard J, CBE psc(j) qwi (ad) .... 13 Mar 09

Sudlow, Andrew J ....29 Mar 09

Stewart, Ian RW, CBE FRAeS BSc jsdc cfs qs ....16 Apr 09

La Forte, Russell W, CBE MBE hcsc(j) psc(j) qab..03 Jul 09

Pentland, Raymond J, QHC BA DPS MTh ....01 Oct 09

Air Commodores - contd.

Lyall, Paul, OBE MA hcsc(j) psc(j) cfs .... 04 Jan 10

Smith, Colin M, psc(j) ....22 Feb 10

Maas, John D, CBE...05 Oct 10

Crayford, Malcolm K, OBE..21 Aug 11

Niven, David M, ...01 Sep 11

Connell, Neil M, OBE psc cfs ....14 Sep 11

Powell, Richard JC, CBE MBA MA FCMI hcsc(j) psc(j) qwi (ad) ....21 Oct 11

Laird, Neil WG, CBE hcsc(j) psc(j)..09 Feb 12

Wren, Simon W..15 Feb 12

Bessell, John C, hcsc(j) psc(j)...27 Apr 12

Bray, Nicholas, CBE MSc MA hcsc(j) psc(j) qab .... 08 Jun 12

McCafferty, Dawn A, psc(j)..20 Aug 12

Patman, Delva F ....01 Nov 12

Huggett, Andrew D, qwi psc...17 Nov 12

Burr, Jonathan, CBE DFC MA BSc hcsc(j) psc(j) cfs .... 10 Dec 12

Duguid, Ian, OBE MiD MA hcsc(j) psc(j) qwi...07 Jan 13

Lee, David JF, BSc MA MSc FInstLM psc(j) cfs...01 Apr 13

Portlock, Jefferson B, psc(j) qab ....19 Apr 13

Richardson, Simon A, psc(j) .... 27 May 13

Andrew, Dean R, OBE hcsc(j) psc(j)... 10 Jun 13

Monro, Seymour HR...22 Jul 13

Dennis, Roderick J, OBE MA...29 Jul 13

Howard, Laurence .... 01 Aug 13

Norman, Victor SE, ...16 Sep 13

Wooding, Jeremy M..16 Sep 13

Marshall, Michael J...01 Nov 13

Wilcock, Stephen J, MBE BEng(Hons) MSc MDA MA CEng........................18 Nov 13

Baldwin, Kevin J.. 13 Jan 14

Spinney, Philip C ....27 Jan 14

Philliban, John .... 31 Jan 14

Vallely, Ian F, OBE MA RAF ....17 Feb 14

Waddington, David J, CBE...06 May 14

Reid, Alastair NC, QHP .... 26 Jun 14

Brazier, Christopher EJ, CBE psc(j) qwi (t) ....10 Jul 14

Mason, Richard D, OBE MA RAF .... 14 Jul 14

Tolfts, Ian R, OBE MA MCIPR...28 Jul 14

Moore, Christopher J, MA BEng(Hons) CEng MIET FCMI ....09 Sep 14

Air Commodores - contd.

Middleton, Jane M	16 Sep 14
Gillespie, Alan K, MA BSc RAF	16 Oct 14
Linter, James E, OBE	18 Nov 14
Howie, Pauline J	03 Dec 14
Hill, Richard, MA FCILT	06 Dec 14
Taylor, Lincoln S, OBE MA BEng(Hons) RAF	11 Dec 14
McMillan, Iain M	14 Dec 14
Kilbey, Stephen C, QHP	19 Dec 14
Bentley, David A	16 Jan 15
Byford, Maria M, BDS MFGDP(UK) MA RAF	07 Apr 15
Bradshaw, Nigel T	13 Apr 15
Phillips, Nigel J, CBE MA MBA CEng MIET RAF	14 May 15
Smyth, Harvey, OBE DFC	28 May 15
Cooper, David G	23 Jun 15
Colman, Nigel J, OBE MA	08 Jul 15
Stringer, John J	03 Aug 15
Lushington, Stephen F, CBE	06 Aug 15
Peel, Charlotte	01 Sep 15
Gale, Ian D, MBE MBA MA CMgr FCMI	10 Sep 15
Alexander, Damian R, CBE BSc MA FCMI RAF	24 Sep 15
Thornber, Steven R, CBE BSc MA	16 Oct 15
Ellard, Simon D, MBA MSc MA BSc FRAeS CEng RAF	13 Nov 15
Reeves, Stephen E	25 Nov 15
Seymour, Alistair J, MA BSc FRAeS FCMI QWI CFS	27 Nov 15
Hay, Nicholas J, OBE MA	08 Jan 16
Wariner, John P, MA BSc CEng FIET RAF	01 Apr 16
Bennett, Lawrence J,	05 Apr 16
Clifford, Richard FJ, OBE	06 May 16
Barrow, Richard P, CBE	02 Jun 16
Walton, Clare S,	13 Jun 16
Sansom, Adam M, MSc BEng CEng MRAeS RAF	24 Jun 16
Gilligan, Mark,	05 Jul 16
Maddison, Richard C, OBE MA RAF	15 Jul 16
Docherty, Charles, MA CEng FRAeS RAF	18 Jul 16
Squires, Peter JM, OBE MA BEng	17 Aug 16
Lloyd, Paul H, MA MDA BEng CEng FIMechE	22 Aug 16
Harris, Simon J,	29 Aug 16

Air Commodores - contd.

Reuter, Justin S, MA ....09 Sep 16

Dixon, Jonathan M, AFC MA BSc(Hons) ....12 Sep 16

Jeffery, Mark A, OBE MA BSc ARCS RAF ....19 Sep 16

Harper, Simon A, OBE MA RAF ....26 Sep 16

Miller, Scott M, MA RAF ....04 Nov 16

Rowland, David J, MA BEng (Hons) CEng MIET RAF ....11 Nov 16

Read, Andrew B, MBA MA BSc CEng FRAeS MAPM RAF ....05 Dec 16

Round, Peter A, MA BSc(Hons) FRAeS ....05 Dec 16

Lloyd, Nicholas J, BSc MA RAF ....08 Dec 16

Smith, Alastair P T ....25 Jan 17

Ball, Julian D, OBE BSc FCMI RAF ....27 Mar 17

McLoughlin, David C, OBE ....27 Mar 17

Steele, Andrew H ....27 Mar 17

Savage, James E, OBE ....18 Apr 17

Corner, Nigel F ....20 Apr 17

Beasant, Anthony J ....24 Apr 17

Attridge, Jeremy J, OBE MSc ....27 Apr 17

Bradshaw, David G, MA BSc ....28 Apr 17

Da'Silva, Colin D ....28 Apr 17

Jennings, Tamra N, OBE ....01 Jun 17

Barnes, Owen RJ, MSc BSc FIMechE CEng ....08 Jun 17

Hunt, Mark, OBE MA MBA FCMI FIMechE CEng ....12 Jun 17

Bruce, Gordon J, MBE MA MBA FCIPD FCIPR RAF ....28 Jun 17

Stamp, Domonic A, ADC MA RAF ....03 Jul 17

Paul, Richard J, BA ....17 Jul 17

Withnall, Richard DJ QHS ....17 Jul 17

Burns, Adrian S ....19 Jul 17

Martin, Andrew T, OBE MDS BSc(Hons) ....21 Jul 17

Smeath, Michael J, MBE ....28 Jul 17

Perkins, Suzanne N ....21 Aug 17

Coton, Catherine C ....04 Spe 17

Moir, Richard D, MA ....18 Sep 17

Godfrey, Paul A, BE ....09 Oct 17

Hunter, James H ....16 Oct 17

Neal-Hopes, Timothy D ....13 Nov 17

O'Neill, Paul E ....30 Nov 17

Gordon, Nicholas J ....04 Dec 17

RAF SQUADRONS

AC - Army Co-operation Squadron

AIR DEFENCE AND AIRBORNE EARLY WARNING

1(F) Squadron
II (AC) Squadron
3 (F) Squadron
6 Squadron
8 Squadron
XI (F) Squadron

AIR TRANSPORT AND AIR REFUELLING

10 Squadron
32 Squadron
47 Squadron
LXX Squadron
99 Squadron
101 Squadron

FLYING TRAINING

IV Squadron
16 Squadron
45 Squadron
56 Squadron
LVII Squadron
60 Squadron
72 Squadron
100 Squadron
115 Squadron
202 Squadron

FORCE PROTECTION

1 Squadron
II Squadron (Parachute)
15 Squadron
34 Squadron
51 Squadron
63 Squadron

OFFENSIVE SUPPORT

IX (B) Squadron
12 Squadron
31 Squadron
617 Squadron

OPERATIONAL CONVERSION UNIT

XXIV Squadron
28 Squadron
29 Squadron
54 Squadron

RECONNAISSANCE

V (AC) Squadron
13 Squadron
14 Squadron
39 Squadron
51 Squadron

SUPPORT HELICOPTER

7 Squadron
18 Squadron
27 Squadron
33 Squadron
84 Squadron
230 Squadron

TEST AND EVALUATION

17 Squadron
41 Squadron
92 Squadron
206 Squadron

EXPLOSIVE ORDNANCE DISPOSAL

5131 (BD)

RECENTLY DISBANDED

15 Squadron
20 Squadron
23 Squadron
25 Squadron
42 Squadron
55 Squadron
78 Squadron
111 Squadron
120 Squadron
201 Squadron
207 Squadron
216 Squadron

RAF RESERVE SQUADRONS

FORCE PROTECTION
3 Tactical Police Squadron RAUXAF
609 (West Riding) RAUXAF
2503 (City of Lincoln) RAUXAF
2620 (County of Norfolk) RAUXAF
2622 (Highland) RAUXAF
2623 (East Anglian) RAUXAF
2624 (County of Oxford) RAUXAF

OPERATIONAL SUPPORT
601 (County of London) VR

LOGISTICS SUPPORT
501 (County of Gloucester) RAUXAF
504 (County of Nottingham) RAUXAF
605 (County of Warwick) RAUXAF

PERSONNEL TRAINING
502 (Ulster) RAUXAF
600 (City of London) RAUXAF
602 (City of Glasgow) RAUXAF
603 (City of Edinburgh) RAUXAF
607 (Country of Durham) RAUXAF
611 (West Lancashire) RAUXAF
614 (County of Glamorgan) RAUXAF

GENERAL SUPPORT
505 Squadron RAUXAF

GROUND SUPPORT
606 (Chilterns) RAUXAF

MEDICAL SUPPORT
612 (County of Aberdeen) RAUXAF

AIR TRANSPORT
4624 (County of Oxford) RAUXAF
622 (Reservist Aircrew) RAUXAF

AEROMEDICAL EVACUATION
4626 (County of Wiltshire) RAUXAF

INTELLIGENCE
7006 (VR)
7010 (VR)
7630 (VR)

MEDIA OPERATIONS
7644 (VR)

RAF SQUADRONS AND BATTLE HONOURS

(Honours marked with an asterisk, may be emblazoned on the Squadron Standard)

1(F) SQUADRON RAF

A winged numeral '1' - approved July 1936 by King Edward VIII.
"In omnibus princeps"- First in all things

Current Station: RAF Lossiemouth, Moray, Scotland, IV31 6SD
Role: Air Defence and Airborne Early Warning

1st Standard presented 24 April 1953 by AVM Sir Charles Longcroft.
2nd Standard presented 27 June 1983 by MRAF Sir Dermot Boyle.

BATTLE HONOURS

Western Front 1915-1918*, Ypres 1915*, Neuve Chappelle, Loos, Somme 1916*, Arras, Ypres 1917, Lys, Amiens, Somme 1918, Hindenburg Line, Independant Force and Germany 1918*, Kurdistan 1922-1925, Iraq 1923-1925, France and Low Countries 1939-1940*, Battle of Britain 1940*, Channel and North Sea 1941-1945, Home Defence 1940-1945, Fortress Europe 1941-1944*, Arnhem, Normandy 1944, France and Germany 1944-1945*, Biscay 1944-1945, Rhine, South Atlantic 1982*, Kosovo, Iraq 2003*.

II (AC) SQUADRON RAF

Three concentric circles over all a Wake Knot - approved by HM King Edward VIII in May 1936.
"Hereward" - 'Guardian of the Army'

Current Station: RAF Lossiemouth, Moray, Scotland, IV31 6SD
Role: Air Defence and Airborne Early Warning

1st Standard presented 31 October 1953 by ACM Sir Robert M Foster.
2nd Standard presented 20 May 1984 by ACM Sir Alasdair Steedman.

BATTLE HONOURS

Western Front 1914-1918*, Mons, Neuve Chappelle*, Ypres 1915*, Loos, Somme 1916*, Arras, Somme 1918, Lys, France and Low Countries 1939-1940*, Dunkirk*, Fortress Europe 1942-1944, France and Germany 1944-1945, Normandy 1944*, Gulf 1991*, Iraq 2003-11, Libya 2011*.

3 (F) SQUADRON RAF

On a monolith, a cockatrice - approved by King George VI in September 1937.
"Tertius primus erit" - The third shall be the first.

Current Station: RAF Coningsby, Lincoln, LN4 4SY
Role: Air Defence and Airborne Early Warning

1st Standard presented 11 December 1953 by ACM Sir Philip Joubert de la Ferte.
2nd Standard presented 3 June 1983 by AM Sir Patrick B Hine.

BATTLE HONOURS

Western Front 1914-1918*, Mons*, Neuve Chapelle, Loos, Somme 1916, Cambrai 1917, Somme 1918*, Hindenburg Line, France and Low Countries 1940*, Battle of Britain 1940*, Home Defence 1940-1945, Fortress Europe 1942-1944, Channel and North Sea 1943-1945, Normandy 1944*, Arnhem*, Rhine, France and Germany 1944-1945*, Iraq 2003*, Libya 2011.

IV SQUADRON RAF

A sun in splendour divided per bend by a flash of lightning - approved by HRH King Edward VIII in May 1936.
"In futurum videre" - To see into the future.

Current Station: RAF Valley, Holyhead,Anglesey, LL65 3NY
Role: Advanced fast-jet flying training

1st Standard presented 31 October 1953 by ACM Sir Robert M Foster.
2nd Standard presented 20 May 1984 by ACM Sir Alasdair Steedman.

BATTLE HONOURS

Western Front 1914-1918*, Mons*, Neuve Chapelle, Somme 1916, Ypres 1917*, Lys, Somme 1918*, France and Low Countries 1939-1940*, Fortress Europe 1942-1944, France and Germany 1944-1945*, Normandy 1944*, Arnhem*, Rhine, Iraq 2003*.

V (AC) SQUADRON RAF

A maple leaf - approved by HM King George VI in June 1937.
"Frangas non flectas" - Thou mayst break but shall not bend me.

Current Station: RAF Waddington, Lincoln, Lincolnshire, LN5 9NB
Role: Reconnaisance

1st Standard presented 24 April 1954 by ACM Sir Leslie N Hollinghurst.
2nd Standard presented 11 August 1983 by AVM G A White.
3rd Standard presented 6 June 2007 by ACM Sir Glenn Torpy

BATTLE HONOURS

Western Front 1914-1918, Mons*, Neuve Chappelle, Ypres 1915*, Loos*, Arras*, Somme 1918*, Amiens*, Hindenburg Line, Waziristan 1920-1925, MOhmand 1927, North West Frontier 1930-1931, North West Frontier 1935-1939, Arakan 1942-1944*, Manipur 1944, Burma 1944-1945*, Libya 2011.

6 SQUADRON RAF

An eagle, wings elevated, preying on a serpent - approved by King George VI in January 1938.
"Oculi exercitus" - The eyes of the Army.

Current Station: RAF Lossiemouth, Moray, Scotland, IV31 6SD
Role: Air Defence and Airborne Early Warning

1st Standard presented 31 January 1954 by AM Sir Claude B R Pelly.
2nd Standard presented 31 October 1980 by ACM Sir Keith Williamson.
3rd Standard presented 1 April 2006 by ACM Sir Jock Stirrup.

BATTLE HONOURS

Western Front 1914-1918*, Neuve Chappelle*, Ypres 1915*, Loos, Somme 1916*, Ypres 1917, Amiens, Hindenburg Line*, Iraq 1919-1920, Kurdistan 1922-1924, Palestine 1936-1939, Egypt and Libya 1940-1943*, El Alamein*, El Hamma, Italy 1944-1945*, South-East Europe 1944-1945, Gulf 1991.

7 SQUADRON RAF

On a hurt, seven mullets of six points forming a representation of the constellation Ursa Major
- approved by King George VI in June 1939.
"Per diem, per noctem" - By day and by night

Current Station: RAF Odiham, Hook, Hampshire, RG29 1QT
Role: Support Helicopter

1st Standard presented 9 October 1953 by MRAF Sir John Salmond.
2nd Standard presented 8 June 1978 by HRH Princess Alice Duchess of Gloucester.
3rd Standard presented 4 May 2004 by HRH The Prince of Wales.

BATTLE HONOURS

Western Front 1915-1918, Ypres 1915, Loos, Somme 1916, Ypres 1917, Fortress Europe 1941-1944, Biscay Ports 1941-1944, Ruhr 1942-1945, German Ports 1942-1945, Berlin 1943-1945, France and Germany 1944-1945, Normandy 1944, Rhine, Kosovo, Iraq 2003*, Iraq 2003-11*.

8 SQUADRON RAF

A sheathed Arabian dagger - approved by King George VI in December 1943.
"Uspiam et passim" - Everywhere unbounded.

Current Station: RAF Waddington, Lincoln, Lincolnshire, LN5 9NB
Role: Reconnaisance (including UK's contribution to the NATO Airbonre Early Warning and Control Force)

1st Standard presented 9 April 1954 by Sir Tom Hickinbotham.
2nd Standard presented 25 February 1967 by His Excellency Sir Richard Turnball.
3rd Standard presented 28 May 1992 by HRH The Duke of Gloucester.
4th Standard presented 2016 by HRH The Earl of Wessex.

BATTLE HONOURS

Western Front 1915-1918, Loos, Somme, Arras, Cambrai 1917, Somme 1918, Amiens, Hindenburg Line, Kurdistan 1922-1924, Aden 1928, Aden 1929, Aden 1934, East Africa 1940-1941, Eastern Waters 1942-1945, Burma 1945, Kosovo, Iraq 2003, Libya 2011.

IX (B) SQUADRON RAF

A bat - approved by King Edward VIII in November 1936.
"Per noctum volamus" - Throughout the night we fly.

Current Station: RAF Marham, Kings Lynn, Norfolk, PE22 9NP
Role: Offensive Support

1st Standard presented 9 October 1956 by AGM Sir Hugh Pughe Lloyd.
2nd Standard presented 23 May 1984 by ACM Sir David Craig.
3rd Standard presented 2009 by AM Sir Stuart Peach.

BATTLE HONOURS

Western Front 1915- 1918*, Somme 1916*, Ypres 1917*, Amiens, Hindenburg Line, Channel and North Sea 1939-1945, Norway 1940, Baltic 1939-1945, France and Low Countries 1940, German Ports 1940-1945, Fortress Europe 1940-1944, Berlin 1941-1945*, Biscay ports 1940-1945, Ruhr 1941-1945, France and Germany 1944-1945, Tirpitz*, The Dams*, Rhine, Gulf 1991*, Kosovo 2003*, Iraq 2003-2011, Libya 2011*.

10 SQUADRON RAF

*A winged arrow - approved by **King George VI in September 1937.***
"Rem acu tangere" - To hit the mark.

Current Station: RAF Brize Norton, Carterton, Oxfordshire, OX18 3LX
Role: Air Refuelling, Air Transport

1st Standard presented 21 October 1958 by HRH The Princess Margaaret.
2nd Standard presented 30 September 1988 by Rt Hon Margaret Thatcher.
3rd Standard presented 30 January 2015 by HRH The Princess Royal.

BATTLE HONOURS

Western Front 1915-1918, Loos, Somme 1916, Arras, Somme 1918, Channel and North Sea 1940-1945, Norway 1940, Ruhr 1940-1945, Fortress Europe 1940-1944, German Ports 1940-1945, Biscay Ports 1940-1945, Berlin 1940-1945, Invasion Ports 1940, France and Germany 1944-1945, Norway 1944, Rhine, Gulf 1991, Iraq 2003-11.

XI (F) SQUADRON RAF

*Two eagles volant in pale - approved by **King George VI in May 1937.***
"Ociores acrierosquaquilis" - Swifter and keener than eagles.

Current Station: RAF Coningsby, Lincoln, LN4 4SY
Role: Air Defence and Airborne Early Warning

1st Standard presented 28 August 1954 by AM Sir Owen Jones.
2nd Standard presented 17 August 1984 by AVM P. S. Collins.

BATTLE HONOURS

Western Front 1915-1918*, Loos*, Somme 1916, Arras, Cambrai 1917*, Somme 1918*, Amiens, Hindenburg Line*, North-West Frontier 1930-1931, North-West Frontier 1935-1939, East Africa 1940, Egypt and Libya 1940-1942*, Greece 1941, Syria 1941, Ceylon April 1942, Arakan 1943-1944*, North Burma 1943-1944*, Manipur 1944, Burma 1944-1945*, Libya 2011.

12 SQUADRON RAF

*A fox's mask - approved by **King George VI in February 1937.***
"Leads the Field"

Current Station: RAF Marham, Kings Lynn, Norfolk, PE22 9NP
Role: Offensive Support

1st Standard presented 23 June 1954 by MRAF The Lord Newall.
2nd Standard presented 21 February 1975 by AM Sir Nigel Maynard.

BATTLE HONOURS

Western Front 1915-1918, Loos*, Somme 1916, Arras, Cambrai 1917*, Somme 1918*, Hindenburg Line, France and Low Countries 1939-1940*, Meuse Bridges*, Fortress Europe 1940-1944, German Ports 1941-1945, Biscay Ports 1940-1945, Berlin 1941-1945*, Ruhr 1941-1945*, France and Germany 1944-1945, Rhine*, Gulf 1991*, Iraq 2003-2011.

13 SQUADRON RAF

In front of a dagger, a lynx's head affrontee - approved by King George VI in February 1937.
"Adjuvamus tuendo" - We assist by watching

Current Station: RAF Waddington, Lincoln, Lincolnshire, LN5 9NB
Role: Reconnaisance

1st Standard presented 3 May 1957 by FM Sir John Harding.
2nd Standard presented 12 February 1993 by HRH The Duke of Kent.

BATTLE HONOURS

Western Front 1915-1918*, Somme 1916, Arras*, Cambrai 1917*, Somme 1918*, Hindenburg Line, France and Low Countries 1939-1940, Dieppe*, North Africa 1942-1943, Mediterranean 1943, Italy 1944-1945*, Gustav Line, Gothic Line, Gulf 1991*, Iraq 2003-2011.

14 SQUADRON RAF

*A winged plate charged with a cross throughout and shoulder pieces of a suit of armour
- approved by King George VI in May 1937.*
"I spread my wings and keep my promise".

Current Station: RAF Waddington, Lincoln, Lincolnshire, LN5 9NB
Role: Reconnaisance

1st Standard presented 21 August 1954 by AVM T. C. Traill.
2nd Standard presented 26 November 1982 by ACM Sir Keith Williamson.

BATTLE HONOURS

Egypt 1915-1917*, Gaza, Megiddo, Arabia 1916-1917*, Palestine 1917-1918*, Transjordan 1924, Palestine 1936-1939, East Africa 1940-1941*, Mediterranean 1941-1943*, Egypt and Libya 1941-1942*, Sicily 1943*, Atlantic 1945*, Gulf 1991, Kosovo.

16 SQUADRON RAF

Two keys in saltire - approved by King Edward VIII in November 1936.
"Operta aperta" - Hidden things are revealed

Current Station: RAF Wittering, Peterborough, Cambridgeshire, PE8 6HB
Role: Initial Pilot Training

1st Standard presented 6 April 1956 by HRH Princess Marina, Duchess of Kent.
2nd Standard presented 12 July 1985 by AVM D. Parry-Evans.

BATTLE HONOURS

Western Front 1915-1918, Neuve Chappelle, Loos, Somme 1916*, Arras*, Ypres 1917*, France and Low Countries 1940, Dunkirk*, Fortress Europe 1943-1944, France and Germany 1944, Normandy 1944*, Arnhem*, Ruhr 1944-1945, Gulf 1991.

17 SQUADRON RAF

A gauntlet.

"Excellere contende" - Strive to excel

Current Station: Edwards Air Force Base California
Role: Test and Evaluation

1st Standard presented 12 July 1960 by MRAF Sir Michael Beetham.
2nd Standard presented 8 February 1985 by AVM Sir Peter Hine.

BATTLE HONOURS

Egypt 1915-1916*, Palestine 1916*, Macedonia 1916-1918*, France & Low Countries 1940*, Dunkirk*, Home Defence 1940, Battle of Britain 1940*, Burma 1942*, Arakan 1943, Burma 1944-1945*, Gulf 1991*

18 SQUADRON RAF

Pegasus rampant - approved by King Edward VIII in May 1936.
"Animo et fide" - With courage and faith.

Current Station: RAF Odiham, Hook, Hampshire, RG29 1QT
Role: Support Helicopter

1st Standard presented 14 June 1962 by HRH The Princess Margaret.
2nd Standard presented 3 February 1989 by ACM Sir Peter Harding.

BATTLE HONOURS

Western Front 1915-1918*, Somme 1916*, Somme 1918*, Hindenburg Line*, Lys, France and Low Countries, Invasion Ports 1940*, Fortress Europe 1940-1942, Channel and North Sea 1940-1941*, Egypt and Libya 1942, North Africa 1942-1943*, Mediterranean 1943, Sicily 1943, Salerno, South East Europe 1943-1944, Italy 1943-1945*, Gothic Line, South Atlantic 1982*, Gulf 1991, Iraq 2003-2011.

XXIV SQUADRON RAF

A Blackcock - approved by HM King George VI in June 1937.

"In omnia parati" - Prepared for all things.

Current Station: RAF Brize Norton, Carterton, Oxfordshire, OX18 3LX
Role: Operational

1st Standard presented 4 March 1954 by AM Sir Charles E N Guest.
2nd Standard presented 15 September 1981 by HRH The Princess Anne.

BATTLE HONOURS

Western Front 1916-1918*, Somme 1916*, Somme 1918, Amiens*, Hindenburg Line*, France and Low Countries 1939-1940*, Malta 1942*, North Africa 1942-1943*, Italy 1943-1944, Burma 1944-1945*, Gulf 1991, Iraq 2003-2011.

27 SQUADRON RAF

An elephant - approved by HM King Edward VIII in October 1936.
"Quam celerrime ad astra" - With all speed to the Stars.

Current Station: RAF Odiham, Hook, Hampshire, RG29 1QT
Role: Support Helicopter

1st Standard presented 7 January 1955 by AVM A E Borton.
2nd Standard presented 22 June 1979 by ACM Sir David Evans.
3rd Standard presented 2007 by Duke of Gloucester.

BATTLE HONOURS

Western Front 1916-1918*, Somme 1916*, Arras, Ypres 1917*, Cambrai 1917*, Somme 1918*, Lys, Amiens, Hindenburg Line, Mahsud 19420, Waziristan 1920-1925, Mohmund 1927, North West Frontier 1930-1931, Mohmund 1933, North West Frontier 1935-1939, Malaya 1941-1942*, Arakan 1942-1944*, North Burma 1944*, Burma 1944-1945, Gulf 1991, Iraq 2003-2011.

28 SQUADRON RAF

In front of a demi-Pegasus, a fasces, approved by HM King Edward VIII in October 1936.
"Quicquid agas age" - Whatsoever you may do, do.

Current Station: RAF Benson, Wallingford, Oxon, OX10 6AA
Role: Operational Conversion Unit

1st Standard presented 16 March 1955 by AM F J Fressanges.
2nd Standard presented 26 June 1977 by HE Sir Murray Maclehose.

BATTLE HONOURS

Italian Front and Adriatic 1917-1918*, Piave, Vittoria Venito, Waziristan 1921-1925*, North-West Frontier 1939*, Burma 1942*, Arakan 1943-1944*, Manipur 1944*, Burma 1944-45*.

29 SQUADRON RAF

An eagle in flight preying on a buzzard.
"Impiger et acer" - Energetic and keen.

Current Station: RAF Coningsby, Lincoln, LN4 4SY
Role: Operational Conversion Unit (Front-line pilots for the Typhoon Force)

1st Standard presented 18 July 1956 by ACM Sir Dermot Boyle.
2nd Standard presented 30 June 1987 by HRH The Princess Margaret.

BATTLE HONOURS

Western Front 1916-1918*, Somme 1916*, Arras, Ypres 1917*, Lys, Somme 1918*, Home Defence 1940-1945*, Battle of Britain 1940*, Channel & North Sea 1939-1940*, Fortress Europe 1943-44, Normandy 1944, France & Germany 1944-45*, Arnhem.

31 SQUADRON RAF

In front of a wreath of laurel, a mullet - approved by King George VI in June 1937.
"In cælum indicum primus" - First into Indian skies

Current Station: RAF Marham, Kings Lynn, Norfolk, PE22 9NP
Role: Offensive Support

1st Standard presented 13 September 1956 by ACM Sir Alec Coryton.
2nd Standard presented 14 November 1986 by AM Sir Leslie Mavor.
3rd Standard presented 29 January 2014 by AM G.W. Bagwell.

BATTLE HONOURS

North West Frontier 1916-1918*, Afghanistan 1919-1920, Mahsud 1919-1920, Waziristan 1919-1925, North West Frontier 1939, Iraq 1941*, Iraq 2003*, Syria 1941, Egypt and Libya 1941-1942*, Burma 1941-1942*, North Burma 1943-1944*, Arakan 1943-1944*, Manipur 1944*, Burma 1941-1942*, Gulf 1991, Kosovo*, Iraq 2003-2011.

32 SQUADRON RAF

A hunting horn stringed - approved by King George VI in December 1936.
"Adeste comites" - Rally round, comrades

Current Station: RAF Northolt, West End Road, Ruislip, London, Middlesex, HA4 6NG
Role: Air Transport

1st Standard presented 6 June 1957 by ACM Sir James M Robb.
2nd Standard presented 6 June 1987 ACM Sir Michael Knight.

BATTLE HONOURS

Western Front 1916-1918, Somme 1916-1918, Arras, Ypres 1917*, Amiens*, France and Low Countries 193-1940*, Battle of Britain 1940*, Home Defence 1940-1942, Dieppe*, North Africa 1942-1943*, Italy 1943, South East Europe 1944-1945*, Gulf 1991, Iraq 2003-2011, Libya 2011.

33 SQUADRON RAF

A hart's head affrontée, couped at the neck - approved by HM King Edward VIII in May 1936.
Loyalty

Current Station: RAF Benson, Wallingford, Oxon, OX10 6AA
Role: Support Helicopter

1st Standard presented 24 April 1958 by ACM Sir Philip Joubert de la Ferte.
2nd Standard presented 19 May 1988 by ACM Sir Denis Smallwood.

BATTLE HONOURS

Home Defence 1916-1918*, Palestine 1936-1939, Egypt and Libya 1940-1943*, Greece 1941*, El Alamein*, France and Germany 1944-1945*, Normandy 1944*, Walcheren*, Rhine*, Gulf 1991*, Iraq 2003-2011*.

39 SQUADRON RAF

A winged bomb.
"Die noctique" - *By day and night*

Current Station: RAF Waddington, Lincoln, Lincolnshire, LN5 9NB
Role: Reconnaisance

1st Standard presented 26 June 1954 by AM Sir Claude B R Pelly.
2nd Standard presented 25 September 1981 by ACM Sir Keith Williamson.
3rd Standard presented 23 January 2008 by AM I Mc Nicoll.

BATTLE HONOURS

Home Defence, 1916-1918, North West Frontier, 1930-1931, Mohmand, 1933, North West Frontier, 1935-1939, East Africa, 1940, Egypt & Libya, 1940-1943, South East Europe, 1944-45, Iraq 2003-2011.

41 SQUADRON RAF

A double-armed cross - approved by HM King George VI in February 1937.
"Seek and Destroy"

Current Station: RAF Coningsby, Lincoln, LN4 4SY
Role: Test and Evaluation

1st Standard presented 14 July 1957 by AM Sir Theodore McEvoy.
2nd Standard presented 5 December 1985 by ACM Sir Peter Harding.
3rd Standard presented 23 September 2011 by ACM Sir Christopher Harper.

BATTLE HONOURS

Western Front 1916-1918*, Somme 1916*, Arras, Cambrai 1917*, Somme 1918*, Lys, Amiens*, Dunkirk, Battle of Britain 1940*, Home Defence 1940-1944*, Fortress Europe 1940-1944*, Dieppe*, France and Germany 1944-1945*, Arnhem, Walcheren, Gulf 1991.

45 SQUADRON RAF

A winged camel - approved by King Edward VIII in October 1936.
"Per ardua surgo" - *Through difficulties I arise.*

Current Station: RAF College Cranwell, Sleaford, Lincolnshire, NG34 8HB
Role: Flying Training

1st Standard presented 9 February 1955 by AM F.J. Fressanges.
2nd Standard presented 4 October 1994 by ACM Sir Andrew Wilson.

BATTLE HONOURS

Western Front 1916-1917*, Somme 1916, Ypres 1917, Italian Front and Adriatic 1917-1918, Piave, Independent Force and Germany 1918*, Kurdistan 1922-1924, Iraq 1923-1925, Egypt and Libya 1940-1942*, East Africa 1940*, Syria 1941, Burma 1942*, Arakan 1943-1944*, Burma 1944-1945*.

47 SQUADRON RAF

In front of a fountain, a demoiselle crane's head erased - approved by King George VI in November 1938.
"Nili nomen roboris omen" - The name of the Nile is an omen of our strength.

Current Station: RAF Brize Norton, Carterton, Oxfordshire, OX18 3LX
Role: Air Refuelling, Air Transport

1st Standard presented 25 March 1955 by MRAF Sir John Slessor.
2nd Standard presented 3 May 1984 by HRH The Princess Anne.
3rd Standard presented 8 June 2006 by HRH The Princess Anne.

BATTLE HONOURS

Macedonia 1916-1918*, East Africa 1940-1941*, Egypt and Libya 1942*, Mediterranean 1942-1943*, Burma 1945*, South Atlantic 1982, Gulf 1991, Iraq 2003-2011*, Libya 2011*.

51 SQUADRON RAF

A goose volant - approved by King George VI in December 1937.
Swift and Sure.

Current Station: RAF Waddington, Lincoln, Lincolnshire, LN5 9NB
Role: Reconnaisance

1st Standard presented 9 July 1968 by ACM Sir Wallace Kyle.
2nd Standard presented 11 November 1999 by HRH The Duke of Gloucester.

BATTLE HONOURS

Home Defence 1916-1918*, Channel and North Sea 1940-1943, Norway 1940*, France and Low Countries 1940, Ruhr 1940-1945*, Fortress Europe 1940-1944, German Ports 1940-1945, Invasion Ports 1940, Biscay Ports 1940-1944, Berlin 1940-1944, Baltic 1940-1944*, Biscay 1942, Italy 1943*, France and Germany 1944-1945*, Normandy 1944, Walcheren, Rhine, South Atlantic 1982, Gulf 1991, Kosovo, Iraq 2003.940-1941*, Egypt and Libya 1942*, Mediterranean 1942-1943*, Burma 1945*, South Atlantic 1982, Gulf 1991, Kosovo, Iraq 2003-2011, Libya 2011.

54 SQUADRON RAF

Lion rampant semée de lys - approved by King George VI.
"Audax omnia perpeti" - Boldness to endure anything.

Current Station: RAF Waddington, Lincoln, Lincolnshire, LN5 9NB
Role: Operational Conversion Unit

1st Standard presented 24 May 1963 by Major K K Horn RFC.
2nd Standard presented 21 January 1988 by ACM Sir Peter Harding.
3rd Standard presented May 2007 by AVM A Pulford.

BATTLE HONOURS

Western Front 1916-1918, Arras*, Ypres 1917, Cambrai 1917*, Amiens*, Home Defence 1940-1945, France and Low Countries 1940, Dunkirk*, Battle of Britain1940*, Fortress Europe 1941*, Eastern Waters 1943-1945*, Gulf 1991.

56 SQUADRON RAF

A phoenix - approved by King Edward VIII in July 1936.
"Quid si coelum ruat" - What if the heavens fall?

Current Station: RAF Waddington, Lincoln, Lincolnshire, LN5 9NB
Role: Flying Training

1st Standard presented 27 April 1956 by HRH Princess Marina, Duchess of Kent.
2nd Standard presented 23 October 1986 by ACM Sir John Rogers.

BATTLE HONOURS

Western Front 1917-1918*, Arras, Ypres 1917*, Cambrai 1917, Somme 1918*, Amiens, Hindenburg Line, France and Low Countries 1940, Dunkirk*, Battle of Britain 1940*, Fortress Europe 1942-1944, Dieppe, France and Germany 1944-1945*, Normandy 1944*, Home defence 1942-1945, Arnhem 1944*.

LVII SQUADRON RAF

Issuant from two logs fesse-wise in saltire a phoenix - approved by King George VI, December 1936.
"Corpus non animum muto" - I change my body, not my spirit.

Current Station: RAF College Cranwell, Sleaford, Lincolnshire, NG34 8HB
Role: Flying Training

1st Standard presented 20 July 1962 by HRH Princess Marina, Duchess of Kent.
2nd Standard presented 1995 by HRH The Princess Royal.

BATTLE HONOURS

Western Front 1916–1918*, Amiens*, France & Low Countries 1939–1940*, Norway 1940*, Channel & North Sea 1940*, Ruhr 1941–1943*, Fortress Europe 1941–1944, Berlin 1941–1943*, Walcheren, France & Germany 1944–1945*, South Atlantic 1982.

60 SQUADRON RAF

A markhor's head - approved by King George VI in December 1937.
"Per ardua ad aethera tendo" - I strive through difficulties to the sky.

Current Station: RAF Shawbury, Shrewsbury, Shropshire, SY4 4DZ
Role: Flying Training

1st Standard presented 6 May 1955 by ACM Sir John Baker.
2nd Standard presented 18 May 1984 by ACM Sir David Lee.

BATTLE HONOURS

Western Front 1916-1918*, Somme 1916*, Arras, Somme 1918, Hindenburg Line*, Waziristan 1920-1925, Mohmand 1927, North West Frontier 1930-1931, Mohmand 1933, North West Frontier 1925-1939, Burma 1914-1942*, Malaya 1941-1942*, Arakan 1942-1944, North Burma 1944, Manipur 1944*, Burma 1944-1945.

LXX SQUADRON RAF

A demi-wing lion erased - approved by King Edward VIII in October 1936.
"Usquam" - Anywhere.

Current Station: RAF Brize Norton, Carterton, Oxfordshire, OX18 3LX
Role: Air Transport

1st Standard presented 16 July 1955 by AVM Sir Hazelton Nicholl.
2nd Standard presented 3 May 1984 by HRH The Princess Anne.

BATTLE HONOURS

Western Front 1916-1918*, Somme 1916*, Arras, Ypres 1917*, Somme 1918, Kurdistan 1922-1924, Iraq 1918-1929, Kurdistan 1930-1931, Northern Kurdistan 1932, North West Frontier 1937, Mediterranean 1940-1943, Egypt and Libya 1940-1943*, Greece 1940-1941, Syria 1941, Iraq 1941*, El Alamein, North Africa 1942-1943*, El Hamma, Sicily 1943, Italy 1943-1945*, Salerno, Anzio and Nettuno, Gustav Line, Gothic Line, South East Europe 1944-1945*, South Atlantic 1982, Gulf 1991, Iraq 2003-2011.

72 SQUADRON RAF

A swift volant - approved by HM King George VI in February 1938.
Swift.

Current Station: RAF Linton-on-Ouse, York, YO30 2AJ
Role: Flying Training

Standard presented 30 June 1966 by AM Sir Ronald Lees.

BATTLE HONOURS

Mesopotamia 1918*, Channel and North Sea 1939-1942, Dunkirk*, Battle of Britain 1940*, Fortress Europe 1941-1942*, North Africa 1942-1943*, Mediterranean 1942-1943, Sicily 1943*, Italy 1943-1945, Salerno*, Anzio and Nettuno*.

84 SQUADRON RAF

A scorpion - approved by King George VI in December 1936.
"Scorpiones pungunt" - Scorpions sting.

Current Station: RAF Akrotiri, Akrotiri, BFPO 57, Cyrpus
Role: Support Helicopter

1st Standard presented 5 January 1956 by ACM Sir Francis Fogarty.
2nd Standard presented 23 October 1980 by AM Sir Keith Williamson.
3rd Standard presented 8 November 2001 by AVM T W Rimmer.

BATTLE HONOURS

Western Front 1917-1918*, Cambrai 1917, Somme 1918*, Amiens, Hindenburg Line*, Iraq 1920, Iraq 1923-1925, Iraq 1928-1929, Egypt and Libya 1940-1942*, Greece 1940-1941*, Iraq 1941*, Habbaniya, Iraq 1941, Malaya 1942*, North Burma 1944*, Manipur 1944.

92 SQUADRON RAF

A cobra entwining a sprig of maple leaf - approved by King George VI in January 1942.
"Aut pugna aut morere"- Either fight or die

Current Station: RAF Waddington, Lincoln, Lincolnshire, LN5 9NB
Role: Test and Evaluation

Standard presented 3 September 1965 by ACM Sir James Robb.

BATTLE HONOURS

Western Front, 1918, Somme, 1918, Hindenburg Line, Amiens, Home Defence, 1940-1941, France & Low Countries, 1940, Battle of Britain, 1940*, Fortress Europe, 1941-1941*, Egypt & Libya, 1942-1943, El Alamein, El Hamma Mediterranean, 1943, Sicily, 1943, Italy, 1943-1945, Anzio & Nettuno, Gustav Line, Gothic Line.

99 SQUADRON RAF

A puma salien.
"Quisque Tenax" - Each One Tenacious.

Current Station: RAF Brize Norton, Carterton, Oxfordshire, OX18 3LX
Role: Air Transport

1st Standard presented 27 September 1957 by ACM Sir Ronald Ivelaw-Chapman.
2nd Standard presented 22 October 2004 by ACM Sir Jock Stirrup.

BATTLE HONOURS

Western Frontier 1918*, Independant Force and Germany 1918, Mahsud, 1919-1920, Waziristan, 1919-1920, German Ports, 1940-1941, Baltic, 1940-1941, France and Low Countries, 1940, Fortress Europe 1940-1942*, Ruhr 1940-1942*, Berlin 1940-42*, Biscay Ports, 1940, Arakan 1942-44, Burma 1944-45, Manipur, 1944, Eastern Waters 1945, Iraq 2003-2011, Ligya 2011.

100 SQUADRON RAF

In front of two bones in saltire, a skull - approved by King George VI in November 1937.
"Sarang tebuan jangan dijolok" - Never stir up a hornet's nest.

Current Station: RAF Leeming, Northallerton, DL7 9NJ
Role: Flying Training

1st Standard presented 21 October 1955 by AM Sir George Mills
2nd Standard presented 14 December 1984 by MRAF Sir Michael Beetham.
3rd Standard presented 2010 by HRH the Duchess of Cornwall.

BATTLE HONOURS

Western Front 1917-1918, Ypres 1917*, Somme 1918*, Independent Force and Germany 1918*, Malaya 1941-1942*, Fortress Europe 1943-1944*, Biscay Ports 1943-1945, Ruhr 1943-1945, Berlin 1943-1945*, German Ports 1943-1945, Baltic 1943-1945, France and Germany 1944-1945, Normandy 1944*, Walcheren.

101 SQUADRON RAF

Issuant from the battlements of a tower, a demi lion rampant guardant
- approved by King George VI in February 1938.
"Mens agitat molem" - Mind over matter.

Current Station: RAF Brize Norton, Carterton, Oxfordshire, OX18 3LX
Role: Air Refuelling, Air Transport

1st Standard presented 14 June 1962 by HRH The Princess Margaret.
2nd Standard presented 24 June 1988 by ACM Sir Peter Harding.
3rd Standard presented 19 September 2013 by HRH The Princess Royal.

BATTLE HONOURS

Western Front 1917-1918*, Ypres 1917*, Somme 1918*, Lys, Hindenburg Line, Fortress Europe 1940-1944*, Invasion Ports 1940*, Ruhr 1940-1945*, Berlin 1941*, Channel and North Sea 1941-1944, Biscay Ports 1941-1944, German Ports 1941-1945, Baltic 1942-1945, Berlin 1943-1944, France and Germany 1944-1945, Normandy 1944*, Walcheren, South Atlantic 1982, Gulf 1991, Kosovo, Iraq 2003-2011, Libya 2011.

115 SQUADRON RAF

A dexter hand erased at the wrist holding a tiller - approved by King George VI in February 1938.
"Despite the elements"

Current Station: RAF Wittering, Peterborough, Cambridgeshire, PE8 6HB
Role: Flying Training - Pilot Instructor Training

1st Standard presented 30 September 1966 by ACM The Earl of Bandon.

BATTLE HONOURS

Independent Force & Germany 1918*, Channel & North Sea 1939–1943*, Norway 1940*, France & Low Countries, German Ports 1940–1945*, Ruhr 1940–1945*, Fortress Europe 1940–1945*, Invasion Ports 1940, Berlin 1940–1945*, Biscay Ports 1940–1943, Baltic 1943, Normandy 1944*, France & Germany 1944–1945, Rhine

202 SQUADRON RAF*

A mallard alighting - approved by King George VI in March 1937.
"Semper vigilate" - Be always vigilant.

(reformed May 2016)*

Current Station: RAF Valley, Holyhead,Anglesey, LL65 3NY
Role: Flying Training - Search and Rescue Training

1st Standard presented 6 September 1957 by AGM Sir Douglas Evill.
2nd Standard presented 16 June 1987 by AGM Sir Peter Terry.

BATTLE HONOURS

Western Front 1916-1918*, Atlantic 1939-1945*, Mediterranean 1940-1943*, North Africa 1942-1943-, Biscay 1942-1943*.

206 SQUADRON RAF

An octopus – approved by King George VI in January 1938
"Nihil nos effugit" — Naught escapes us

Current Station: RAF Brize Norton, Carterton, Oxfordshire, OX18 3LX
Role: Test and Evaluation - Heavy Aircraft Test and Evaluation Squadron

1st Standard presented 28 July 1966 by HRH The Princess Margaret.
2nd Standard presented 21 May 1992 by HRH The Duke of Edinburgh.

BATTLE HONOURS

Western Front 1916-1918*, Arras 1917*, Lys, Channel and North Sea 1939-1945*, Atlantic 1939 and 1941-1945*, Dunkirk, Invasion Ports 1940, Fortress Europe 1940 and 1942*, German Ports 1940 and 1942, Biscay 1941 and 1943-1944*, Bismarck*, Baltic 1945, South Atlantic 1982, Gulf 1991, Iraq 2003-2011

230 SQUADRON RAF

In front of a palm tree eradicated, a tiger passant guardant
- approved by King George VI in February 1937.
"Kita chari jauh" (Malay) - We search far.

Current Station: RAF Benson, Wallingford, Oxon, OX10 6AA
Role: Operational Support Helicopter

1st Standard presented 26 October 1962 by HRH The Duke of Gloucester.
2nd Standard presented 27 October 1992 by HRH The Duke of Gloucester.

BATTLE HONOURS

Home Waters 1918*, Mediterranean 1940-1943*, Egypt and Libya 1940-1943*, Greece 1940-1941*, Malta 1940-1942*, Eastern Waters 1943-1945*, North Burma 1944*, Burma 1945*, Gulf 1991, Iraq 2003-2011*.

617 SQUADRON RAF

On a roundel, a wall in fesse, fracted by three flashes of lightning in pile and issuant from the breach water proper
- approved by King George VI in March 1944.
"Aprés moi, le déluge" - After me, the flood.

Current Station: RAF Lossiemouth, Moray, Scotland, IV31 6SD *(will be based in RAF Marham from 2018)*
Role: Air Defence and Airborne Early Warning

1st Standard presented 14 May 1959 by HM Queen Elizabeth The Queen Mother.
2nd Standard presented 31 January 1988 by HM Queen Elizabeth The Queen Mother.

BATTLE HONOURS

Fortress Europe 1943-1945*, The Dams*, Biscay Ports 1944*, France and Germany 1944-1945*, Normandy 1944*, Tirpitz*, Channel and North Sea 1944-1945*, German Ports 1945*, Gulf 1991, Iraq 2003-2011.

ROYAL AIR FORCE REGIMENT

"THE ROCK APES"

"Per Ardua" - Through Adveristy.

(Based at: RAF Honington, Suffolk)

Commandant General -
Air Cdre Richard F J Clifford *OBE*..Apr 16

FIELD SQUADRONS

1 Squadron
II Squadron (Parachute)
15 Squadron
34 Squadron
51 Squadron
63 Squadron (Queen's Colour Squadron)

CHEMICAL, BIOLOGICAL, RADIOLOGICAL, NUCLEAR (CBRN) OPERATIONS SQUADRONS

26 Squadron
27 Squadron

OTHER UNITS: FORCE PROTECTION

RAF Force Protection - HQ at RAF Honington
No. 2 Force Protection Wing - RAF Leeming
No. 3 Force Protection Wing - RAF Marham
No. 4 Force Protection Wing - RAF Brize Norton
No. 5 Force Protection Wing - RAF Lossiemouth
No. 7 Force Protection Wing - RAF Coningsby
No. 20 RAF Regiment Wing - RAF Honington CBRN

ROYAL AUXILIARY AIR FORCE REGIMENT SQUADRONS

504 County of Nottingham Squadron RAuxAF
609 Squadron RAF (West Riding) RAuxAF
2503 Squadron (County of Lincoln)
2620 Squadron (County of Norfolk)
2622 Squadron (Highland)
2623 Squadron (East Anglian) (CBRN)
2624 Squadron (County of Oxford)

1 SQUADRON RAF REGIMENT

- approved by King George VI - August 1939

Swift and Sudden.

Current Station: RAF Honington, Suffolk
Role: Force Protection

1st Standard Presented 8 April 1959 by AM Sir Hugh Constantine
2nd Standard Presented 3 November 1988 by AM Sir Anthony Skingsley
3rd Standard Presented 2013 by ACM Sir Stephen Dalton

BATTLE HONOURS

Kurdistan 1922-1923, Kurdistan 1930-1931, Palestine 1936, Habbaniya, Iraq 1941, Egypt & Libya 1941- 943*, Gulf 1991*, Former Yugoslavia Jun 1995, Bosnia Jun 1997, Kuwait Feb 1999, Iraq 2003-2011.

II SQUADRON (PARACHUTE) RAF REGIMENT

A winged wheel or - approved by King Edward VIII - August 1936

"Nunquam Non Paratus" - Never Unprepared.

Current Station: RAF Honington, Suffolk
Role: Force Protection

1st Standard Presented 25 November 1959 by ACM Sir Hubert Patch.
2nd Standard Presented 5 June 1989 by ACM Sir Patrick Hine.

BATTLE HONOURS

Transjordan 1924, Palestine 1936-1939, Egypt & Libya 1940-1943*, Iraq 1941*, Syria 1941*, El Alamein*, North Africa 1943*, Iraq 2003, Iraq 2003-2011.

15 SQUADRON RAF REGIMENT

A scorpion with tail erect set in front of an infantry bayonet.

"Yang Pertama Di-Mana Mana" - To be reckoned with anywhere.

Current Station: RAF Honington, Suffolk
Role: Force Protection

1st Standard presented 10 October 1975 by ACM Sir Andrew Humphrey.
2nd Standard presented 7 October 2005 by AVM Barry Thornton.

BATTLE HONOURS

Gulf 1991, Former Yugoslavia, Bosnia, Kuwait, Iraq 2003.

26 SQUADRON RAF REGIMENT

- approved by Queen Elizabeth II - July 1975.

"Action - Reaction"

Current Station: RAF Honington, Suffolk
Role: Chemical, Biological, Radiologoical and Nuclear Capability(CBRN) Operations Squadron

Standard presented 28 November 1979 by AM Sir Peter Terry.

BATTLE HONOURS

Gulf 1991, Iraq 2003-2011*

27 SQUADRON RAF REGIMENT
- approved by Queen Elizabeth II - April 1977.
"Defensores Defendo" - I defend the defender.

Current Station: RAF Honington, Suffolk
Role: Chemical, Biological, Radiologoical and Nuclear Capability(CBRN) Operations Squadron

Standard presented 4 June 1980 by ACM Sir David Evans.

BATTLE HONOURS
The squadron does not have any battle honours at this time.

34 SQUADRON RAF REGIMENT
- approved by Queen Elizabeth II - July 1973.
"Feu de Fer" - Fire from iron.

Current Station: RAF Leeming, North Yorkshire
Role: Force Protection

1st Standard presented 4 October 1979 by ACM Sir David Evans.
2nd Standard presented 20 May 1999 by ACM Sir Peter Squire.

BATTLE HONOURS

Gulf 1991, Iraq 2003-11*.

51 SQUADRON RAF REGIMENT
"Celeriter Defendere" - Swift to defend.

Current Station: RAF Lossiemouth, Moray
Role: Force Protection

1st Standard presented 22 December 1977 by AM P.D.G. Terry.
2nd Standard presented 9 September 2003 by HRH The Duke of York.

BATTLE HONOURS

France and Germany 1944-1945*, Gulf 1991, Iraq 2003*, Iraq 2003-2011.

63 SQUADRON (QUEEN'S COLOUR SQUADRON) RAF REGIMENT
"Vigilo et Arceo" - Vigilant and Secure

Current Station: RAF Northolt, West End Road, Ruislip, London, Middlesex, HA4 6NG
Role: Dual role - Force Protection and Queen's Colour Squadron (drill and ceremonial element of the RAF Regiment)

1st Standard presented 27 May 1976 by HRH The Princess Anne.
2nd Standard presented 2009 by ACM Sir Richard Johns

BATTLE HONOURS

Italy 1943-44, France & Germany 1945, South Atlantic 1982*, Iraq 2003-2011.

IMPORTANT NOTES CONCERNING RAF BATTLE HONOURS

The Battle Honours to which Royal Air Force Squadrons are entitled, and the conditions under which they are awarded are set out in AP 3327, originally published in 1957.

T he Battle Honours Committee was first convened in 1947 to consider Honours for World War 1, World War 2 and the Inter War Years, however, since the Army did not then award honours for battles between the wars the RAF fell in step and considered just World War 1 and World War 2. These recommendations were approved by the Air Council in AC 58 (47) of Nov 47.

The Standard will be awarded by order of the Monarch in every case, to Operational Squadrons qualifying in one of the following two respects:

1. By completion of 25 years of existence in the RAF, the Royal Flying Corps or the Royal Naval Air Service. This includes Squadrons with continuous or non-continuous service.

2. By having earned the Monarch's appreciation of specially outstanding operations .

Battle Honours awarded for operations during the First and Second World Wars, up to maximum of 8 in number, maybe displayed on Squadron Standards. If a Squadron has been awarded more than 8, the Squadron Commander is to select those, which are to be displayed. Battle Honours for operations during the period between the two wars were awarded to Squadrons but may not be emblazoned on Standards. Battle Honours awarded for operations occuring after the Second World War have been awarded both with and without the right to emblazonment. Only those Battle Honours with the Sovreign's permission to emblazon may be displayed but subject to a maximum of 15.

It was also agreed that only flying squadrons were entitled to receive a Squadron Standard, however in January 1 952 Standards were to be awarded to RAF Regiment and Royal Auxiliary Air Force Squadrons.

The first Squadron to receive its Standard was No 1 Squadron and the first Regiment Squadron to receive its Standard was No 2 Armoured Car Company RAF Regiment.

Since 1945, 5 Battle Honours have been granted namely, " Korea 1950-1953", "South Atlantic 1982", "Gulf 1991 " , " Kosovo" and " Iraq 2003". However, no right to emblazonment was granted in the case of "Korea 1950-1953", and the three Squadrons awarded their Battle Honours in 1987 have been disbanded in the intervening years. In the case of "South Atlantic 1982" 3 precedents were created;

a . For the first time, authority was given to emblazon an honour awarded outside the time frame of the 2 World Wars.

b. The right to emblazon was accorded to 3 Squadrons only (Numbers 1 and 18 Squadrons and Number 63 Squadron RAF Regiment) rather than being extended to all the Squadrons which were granted the Battle Honour, thus creating a two-tier Battle Honours system . The review of post-war operations conducted in 1987 considered that a distinction should be drawn between the award of the Battle Honours and the right of emblazonment. It was decided that the latter should be the ultimate accolade and be reserved to those Squadrons which were in direct confrontation with the enemy and had demonstrated gallantry and spirit under fire.

For seniority purposes an RAF Regiment Squadron is entitled to claim its service as an armoured car squadron.

OBITUARY

ACTIVE LIST

Officers and Warrant Officers
Whose deaths have been reported since September 2007

Rank and Name   Date of Death

2015

Flight Lieutenant

Scott, Alan (PILOT)...11 Oct 2015

Roberts, Geraint (OPS SPT(REGT)) ....11 Oct 2015

2014

Flight Lieutenant

Chauhan, Rekesh (Intelligence branch)..27 Apr 2014

2011

Squadron Leader

Downing, Anthony (Engineer Branch)..23 Dec 2011

INDEX

ROYAL INDEX

PERSONNEL INDEX

Index of RAF officers and other senior appointment holders.

(Some entries of RAF officers (actively serving and retired) do not list their personal service numbers as at the time of publication their numbers could not be confirmed.)